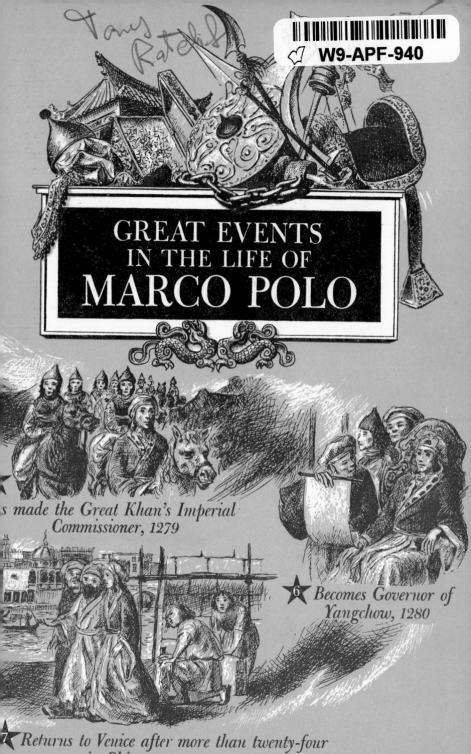

GREAT EVENTS
IN THE LIFE OF
MARCO POLO

...s made the Great Khan's Imperial
Commissioner, 1279

★ 6 Becomes Governor of
Yangchow, 1280

★ Returns to Venice after more than twenty-four
years in China, 1295

THE STORY OF
Marco Polo

And so the thrilling voyage began

THE STORY OF
Marco Polo

By OLIVE PRICE

Illustrated by FEDERICO CASTELLON

ENID LAMONTE MEADOWCROFT
Supervising Editor

PUBLISHERS Grosset & Dunlap NEW YORK

COPYRIGHT, 1953, BY OLIVE PRICE

The Story of Marco Polo

PRINTED IN THE UNITED STATES OF AMERICA

Library of Congress Catalog Card No. 53–8125

*This book of adventure
is for my brother*
MILTON
*who likes adventures
of his own!*

Contents

Illustrations

ILLUSTRATIONS

THE STORY OF
Marco Polo

"Begone!" one man shouted. *"You spoil my fruit!"*

CHAPTER ONE

The Painted Galley

"Today's the day!" cried Marco Polo, a dark-eyed boy nine years old.

He leaped out of bed as he heard the church bells of San Marco ring. Christopher, his cousin, still snug and warm, slept on. He had come to visit Marco's home in Venice, Italy. His own home on his father's farm was many miles away.

Marco pulled aside the yellow silk draperies which hung at a casement window, and looked down on a wide canal. There were few streets in Venice. Almost every passage through the city was a winding waterway.

Marco's home was in a fine part of the town. It was large and filled with beautiful things. Marco lived there with his mother and their faithful servants.

The rose-colored light of early morning softly lighted the big room. Marco picked up a pillow from a deep window seat. Mischievously he aimed it right at Christopher's nose. Christopher sat up blankly as it landed on his face.

"Wh-where am I?" he sputtered, pushing the pillow aside.

"You are in Venice, bambino!" Marco cried. "And today is to be a wonderful day!"

Christopher swung his legs to the side of the bed, meanwhile rubbing his eyes.

"You are like the rooster in my father's barnyard," he grumbled. "You crow too early in the morning!"

Marco laughed at him.

"It is not often that my tutor gives me a day off from lessons," he said. "And he has my mother's permission to take us to the Arsenal to watch the workmen building the new galley!"

"It would be nice," said Christopher, "if we could go by ourselves. Why must your tutor go with us?"

Marco explained this reasonably enough.

"We can't get into the Arsenal if Signor Gilberto isn't with us. It's the biggest shipbuilding place in Venice. And boys aren't usually allowed to visit it."

Christopher was now wide awake.

"It will be fun to see it," he said, "even if it is so early in the morning!"

Marco opened the casement wide.

"We are not the only ones who are up. Listen!"

Voices came up from the waters below. The canal was dotted with small boats loaded with produce from the market place.

"Peppers and plums!" an Italian voice called. "Fresh fish! Just caught in the sea!"

Christopher hurried across the room to Marco. The boys leaned over the casement sill.

"That is Tony," said Marco. "Tony! Tony!" he shouted. "Throw me a plum!"

"Ah, Marco! Good morning!" Tony called.

He stood at the stern of a boat, propelling it with a long pole. The boat was piled high with baskets of golden yellow oranges. Luscious purple grapes. Tawny-colored figs. Tony poled his boat skillfully between other boats until it was almost under Marco's window.

"Catch the plum, Marco!" he called. "Catch!"

[5]

Marco cupped his hands together. A big purple plum sailed through the air. Marco caught it gaily.

"Santa Maria!" laughed Tony. "You never miss!"

"Venice is strange," murmured Christopher, watching Tony pole his boat back to

midstream. "On my father's farm, we have roads to walk on. Here everyone goes everywhere in a boat!" His eyes rested on a graceful black boat being propelled by a man who stood in the stern and rowed with a single oar. "There's a gondola, Marco. I'd like to ride in a gondola."

"That's good," said Marco, "because we'll be riding in one to the Arsenal. Here, have a bite of this plum."

A knock on the door interrupted their chatter. An old family servant, Rosa, stood on the threshold. She carried a blue-and-gold pitcher.

"Good morning, boys!" She greeted them with a big smile. "Here is warm water to wash with."

She poured the water into a wash bowl that stood on a chest of drawers.

"You are to wear your blue tunic," she reminded Marco. "You must look well if you are to be seen at the Arsenal."

"Is Signor Gilberto up yet?" asked Marco, splashing water in his face.

"He's already waiting for breakfast," Rosa laughed good-naturedly. "And cook's just baking the bread sticks!"

Signor Gilberto was not the grim person

[7]

Christopher had feared he might be. He was tall and looked like a learned gentleman, but his eyes often twinkled under his shaggy eyebrows. He enjoyed seeing boys having fun, especially if they had earned it by learning their lessons well. Today he was determined that Marco and his visitor should have a happy holiday.

They set off soon after breakfast. As they rode in the gondola, the boys chattered gaily, sometimes both at once. It was adventurous to be on the Grand Canal on this lovely April morning. The canal seemed alive with shouting and singing. Drops of water from the oars of gondoliers fell like diamonds sparkling in the sun.

"I'm counting gondolas!" cried Christopher. "You count them too, Marco. It's fun!"

Suddenly he dodged as the air seemed to be churning with the beat of wings. Hundreds of pearly pigeons flew down from the lofty spires of St. Mark's Cathedral. Their bright eyes sought gondolas which carried fruit and vegetables. Gondoliers on the boats which surrounded Marco's were frantic. Angry voices echoed up and down the Grand Canal.

"Begone! Begone! You birds of the devil!"

one man shouted. "You spoil my fruit! Be-gone!"

The boys watched the boatmen beat off the birds with their oars. The chattering pigeons spread their many-colored wings and flew back in a cloud of feathers to the shelter of St. Mark's.

The gondola in which the boys were riding passed under a stone bridge. There were street musicians on the bridge, playing mandolins. Tiny girls were dancing and singing. Boys were playing marbles and calling each other names. Presently Marco pointed to a glittering palace built of rich red marble.

"There's the Palace of the Doges," he told Christopher. "They're the rulers of Venice."

"I would like to show my mother the pal-ace," Christopher said, admiring its graceful columns.

"Soon now," Signor Gilberto was saying, "we will be out of the city and heading for the Arsenal. It is built on an island, Christopher, just like the rest of Venice. There are one hun-dred and twenty islands in all."

Marco was growing impatient. He urged the gondolier to hurry until at last the fellow cried: "Santa Maria, Marco Polo! This is a

[9]

gondola, not a galley with the speed of twenty oars!"

Signor Gilberto rebuked Marco mildly. "The man is rowing as fast as he can! Patience, Marco. We will soon be at the Arsenal."

At last it was really in sight. They could hear activity before they saw it. The ringing of bells. The beat of hammers. The voices of the men who were making the sails. Marco stood up in the gondola so suddenly that it rocked from side to side.

"There it is, Christopher! There is the Arsenal! There are docks and warehouses and lumber yards! And the mast-makers' shops and foundries! And wait till you see the place where they make the guns!"

Christopher laughed at Marco's enthusiasm, but he, too, was eager to see all this. Marco sniffed like a hunting dog, as the gondolier stopped his boat.

"Smell, Christopher!" Marco commanded. "The spice ships are in from Egypt! Can't you smell pepper and cloves?"

Christopher sniffed and found the air fragrant. He had to hurry to keep up with Marco, who was already out of the gondola and running toward the docks.

They came to the spot where a new galley
was being completed

All morning they inspected the Arsenal. A guide went with them and told them about the wonderful way in which ships were built.

It was almost noon before they came to the spot where a new galley was being completed. It was a splendid ship. Marco pointed upward to a sail which was unfurled. A picture of a great red lion had been painted upon it. Above the lion were the words: "The Year of our Lord, Twelve Hundred and Sixty-Three."

"Look at the lion!" exclaimed Marco. "He ought to guard the ship well."

"It is the lion of St. Mark," said the guide.

"The lion of St. Mark," repeated Marco. "He has a ferocious look in his eyes."

He and Christopher climbed eagerly aboard the galley. They walked the deck and explored the cabins and sat on benches where galley slaves would sit to pull their oars.

The hours passed very quickly. All too soon for both the boys, they had to leave the Arsenal and start on their way home.

When Marco reached the house, he raced to his mother's room to tell her all about his exciting day. She was sitting on the window seat, watching the play of afternoon shadows on the canal below. Marco thought she looked very pretty in her richly embroidered blue dress.

"Oh, Mamma mia!" he breathed, "it was wonderful! Wonderful! I wish that I could sail away on a painted galley!"

His young mother looked thoughtful. "Perhaps one day you will," she said softly. "Your father's business makes him a wanderer to many lands. Perhaps the urge to travel is already in your blood."

Suddenly his mother sighed. Marco did

not need to be told why she looked sad. It had been such a long time since she had seen his father—more than nine years. And Marco had never seen him at all! His father had gone on a dangerous trading trip to the Far East a few months before Marco was born.

"I wish that I could see my father," Marco said slowly. "I wish that he could live with us."

His mother laid her hand upon his shoulder. "Your father is a merchant," she said, "and that is why he must spend so much time in foreign lands."

"Rosa says," added Marco, "that he is a noble Venetian with a seat in the great council that helps to make the laws."

His mother smiled as she smoothed his hair. "Rosa is right, Marco mio. Your father is a noble Venetian and also a very brave man."

"But when will he come home?"

"I hope that it will be soon." His mother almost whispered the words as she watched the evening star break through the clouds above the canal. Marco had often wished on this star. Now, he glanced at his mother again and saw the faraway look in her eyes.

He made a fervent wish that his father would come home safely.

[*14*]

CHAPTER TWO

The Homecoming

T HIS blade looks rusty and it's almost new!"
Marco grumbled as he unsheathed his sword.

His sword master frowned. Three times a
week he came to the house to give Marco lessons in fencing.

"You are fifteen years old now, Marco," he
said, "and expected to keep your own sword
shining. It is part of a young nobleman's train-
ing." After a moment, he added, "Your riding
master tells me that you ride very well, and
that you seem to have a special way with animals. I want you to handle a sword well too."

Marco felt a bit guilty. He had not polished
his sword because he had neglected it. He had
been spending every free hour at the Arsenal.
It was growing larger day by day. And more
galleys were coming to Venice than ever be-

fore. They brought fascinating cargoes from India and China and other Eastern countries.

Once Marco had seen a herd of white horses brought in from the plains of Arabia. Another time, there had been fifty wild-eyed falcons, looking so fierce that they had almost frightened him. And only the day before he had seen galley slaves struggling to carry heavy chests filled with pearls from the China Sea.

"Marco!" His sword master was speaking sharply. "Polish your sword and let us begin!"

Marco had scarcely finished this task when a voice called from the hall.

"Marco! Marco!"

The sword master looked around quickly. "Who is that calling you like a street urchin?" he asked.

Marco suddenly grinned.

"That is my cousin Christopher," he replied. "He has come to visit me again, and will stay a whole month!"

The door to the gymnasium was flung wide open. Christopher had not bothered to knock. His eyes were bright with excitement.

"Marco!" he cried again, ignoring the sword master. "There's been a message! Your father's coming home!"

"My—my father!" Marco suddenly turned pale.

"Ask Rosa!" said Christopher. "She is on her way upstairs to tell you, but I got here first!"

Marco was so surprised that he was unable to utter a sound. He simply stood staring wide-eyed at Christopher, holding on to his sword. He was clutching it so tightly that the blood drained from his fingers and they looked as white as his face. At last he said slowly:

"I have never seen my father."

"Bambino!" Rosa came panting into the room and laid her hand on his arm. "Your father is coming home after all these years! Oh, how I wish that your gentle mother had lived to see this day!"

Marco was taller than Rosa now, so she had to stand on tiptoe to embrace him. She could feel his body draw up tensely as though he were a race horse on the starting line.

"I wish that she were here, too," he said sadly. "She was always so lonely for him."

Tears filled his eyes. He had loved his pretty mother deeply. Even though she had died several years earlier, he still missed her very much.

Rosa made the sign of the cross.

"Blessings on her memory, Marco," she said. "Your gentle mother was an angel! But do not cry, my bambino. She would want you to be glad to see your father. She would want you to greet him happily, without tears for her absence. And who knows, Marco? Who can tell? Maybe she knows about this meeting and is happy too."

Marco looked at Rosa gravely.

"Perhaps you are right," he said. After a moment, he asked, "When did this news come?"

"A servant from another great house in Venice brought it!" Christopher exclaimed. "He said his master had just returned from Egypt. He met your father in Cairo. He asked him to tell you that he and your uncle Maffeo will arrive here in about a month."

"That's only four weeks from now," Rosa added.

"Only four weeks!" repeated Marco. "In only four more weeks I shall see my father!"

His sword master came forward.

"That should give you time to perfect your manners with the sword," he said. "I am sure that your father will want to see you as skillful

[*18*]

with your hands as you are with your brain."
He laid a kindly hand on Marco's shoulder.
"Come, lad! Let us go on with our lesson."

As Rosa left the gymnasium, Christopher
sat down, cross-legged, on the floor. He was
almost as tall as Marco now and his muscles
were strong from the work he had done on his
father's farm. He watched the swordplay im-
patiently until the lesson was over. The sword
master had scarcely left the room when Christopher jumped to his feet.

"I am as excited about your father's home-
coming as you are, Marco!" he cried.

"I hope that my father will like me," Marco
said soberly. Then his eyes shone. "We will
have such fun together! There are many things
to show him! My fawn-colored horse at the
riding school—all the new things at the Arsenal—and we should give a party for him—"

"A big party!" added Christopher.

The boys were kept very busy until the
day the ship was sighted which was bringing
Marco's father home. News came from the
Arsenal that it would arrive late that afternoon. There was much hustle and bustle all
through the house. Relatives were gathering
there to welcome Marco's father and uncle.

He watched the swordplay until the lesson was over

Plans for the big party were going ahead at top speed. Savory fowls were being roasted. Rich pastries were being baked. Yards and yards of spaghetti were drying in the kitchen. Sparkling bottles of red wines and white wines were being brought up from the wine cellars.

Christopher was watching Marco dress to meet his father.

"You're as nervous as a cat!" he said.

Marco looked annoyed.

"Wouldn't you be?" he demanded. "Suppose that you had never met your father in your whole life?"

Christopher shrugged his broad young shoulders. "I guess I'd be nervous too. I wonder what he will look like."

"It isn't what *he* will look like to me!" snapped Marco. "It's what *I* will look like to him!"

As Rosa came in with the velvet suit that Marco had chosen to wear, the boy's thoughts were whirling with unanswerable questions. What will my father expect of me? Will I be dressed right? Will I be strong and tall enough to please him?

He was so occupied with his thoughts that he did not hear Signor Gilberto come in.

"Marco!" Signor Gilberto's voice was a bit shaky.

"Yes, Signor," Marco answered.

"Your father has already arrived. He is asking to see you in the library."

"But he can't be here! He can't be!" Marco exclaimed. "I wanted to meet his galley when it came into the Arsenal!"

Signor Gilberto laid a friendly hand on Marco's shoulder. "The weather was fairer than expected," he told him. "There were easterly winds all the way. The galley sailed in sooner than anyone believed possible."

Marco's eyes sought his tutor's imploringly.

"What does my father look like?" he asked.

Signor Gilberto smiled. "Go down and see, Marco. Go down and see!"

Marco dressed quickly and went downstairs. The heavy oak door to the library was closed. He paused before he laid his hand on the wrought-iron latch. He felt shy and ill at ease.

"Are you afraid to open the door?" he mocked himself. "Are you afraid to meet your own father?"

He was angry because he was fearful, but at last he flung the door wide open.

A tall, handsome man dressed in a rich wine-

colored cloak and tunic was standing in front
of a fireplace.

"Bambino!" he exclaimed. "Marco, my
son!"

"Father!" Marco cried joyfully.

He found himself locked in his father's embrace. A moment later his father was saying,
"But you are not a bambino! You are tall and
grown up! Your body is strong and you have
the look of a bright new coin!"

Marco's shyness was gone now. He felt like
strutting like a peacock! It was wonderful to
know that his father was looking upon him
with love and approval.

"I am happy that you have come home at
last," he said.

His father waved him to a chair placed near
a richly carved table. There was an iron can-
dlelabra with unlighted candles upon it. When
Marco passed the table his flowing sleeve
brushed by the candles. All seven of them
tumbled down to the floor. Immediately he
was embarrassed. How awkward his father
must think him! He did not feel like strutting
now. "Managia!" he said crossly. "I am as
clumsy as a peasant!"

His father laughed aloud.

"What lad of fifteen is not?" he asked. "You are like a colt, Marco. But have patience. You have plenty of time to learn to walk sedately!"

For almost an hour Marco and his father talked. It was a deeply satisfying thing for Messer Nicolo Polo to become acquainted with his son. For Marco it was thrilling to hear his father mention the cities and countries through which he had journeyed. Names of far places seemed to drop from his lips like the sound of bugles. Bagdad. Alexandria. Golden Kanbalu in mysterious Cathay, which was the ancient name for China.

His father told him something about all these places. He told him also of Kublai Khan, who was the Emperor of Cathay, the greatest and richest emperor in the whole world.

"Kublai Khan rules Cathay with dignity and wisdom," said Messer Polo. "Your uncle and I spent three years at his court. We taught him the ways of the Western world and he taught us much about the East."

"You will miss these people and places, Father," Marco said soberly, "now that you are back in Venice."

His father smiled mysteriously.

"I will not miss them as much as you may suppose," he said. "Your uncle Maffeo and I will not be in Venice long. We are here on a mission for the great Kublai Khan and will soon return to Cathay."

Marco looked so disappointed on hearing this news that his father tousled his hair and laughed. "Do not look so gloomy, my son."

"But—but, Father," said Marco, "I have longed so much for your return and now—"

His father's voice was tender.

"And I have longed to be with you." Suddenly he laid his hand on Marco's shoulder. "The memory of your mother is deeply engraved on my heart. She, too, would wish us to be together. I think—"

"But if you go away," interrupted Marco, "how can we be together?"

For a moment his father looked at him in silence. Then he said happily: "We can be together, Marco, because I am going to take you with me!"

"I am to go to Cathay!" Marco was so startled, he suddenly leaped to his feet.

"You are to go to Cathay," said his father. "It may be a dangerous journey. The trip will be long and hard—and there will doubtless be things that will terrify you on the way—"

Marco shrugged his shoulders and laughed. "Who cares about the danger!" he cried. "I won't be afraid! Wait until you see how well I can handle a sword!"

There was a sudden sound of clapping hands and a man said: "Good, Marco! Good! That is the way a brave lad should talk!"

Marco's father smiled as he saw his brother Maffeo standing in the doorway.

"This is your uncle Maffeo," he told the boy.

Marco crossed the room to his uncle, who opened his arms to receive him.

"We shall be great friends," he said. "Very great friends indeed."

"Of course we shall," said Marco, liking his uncle at once.

Messer Maffeo smiled.

"I really came to tell you both that if we do not hurry we shall be late for the party. We had better join our guests at once."

Marco did not look pleased at this idea.

"What's the matter?" his uncle asked. "Don't you want to go to the party?"

"Yes, I want to go to the party," Marco answered. "But I'd really like to find Christopher first. I want to tell him right away that I am to go to Cathay!"

"Very well, my son," said his father. "Go and find Christopher. We will see you later."

He looked at his brother and laughed as Marco rushed out of the room, calling his cousin excitedly: "Christopher! Christopher! Christopher!"

CHAPTER THREE

Off to Cathay

T HERE it is!" cried Marco, looking up at the big armed galley rocking in its berth. "And it's almost ready to sail! Oh! I'm so excited!"

"I would be too," said Christopher, "if I were off to Cathay!"

Marco's father and Uncle Maffeo had already gone aboard the ship. Marco still lingered on the quay. He wanted a few more words with Signor Gilberto, Rosa, and Christopher, who had come down to the Arsenal to say a last farewell. At any moment now the galley's sails would be billowing in the wind. And the ship would be on its way across the blue Adriatic Sea.

The boys really hated to part. Marco laid an affectionate hand on Christopher's arm.

"I wish you were going with me," he said. "It would be so much fun to sail together."

Christopher's brown eyes shone.

"I hope someday that we will," he answered.

Rosa looked sober as she said: "It makes me sad, bambino, to see you so glad to sail away."

Signor Gilberto smiled.

"This is what he has dreamed of, Rosa! Ever since Marco was a little boy, he has wanted to sail away on a painted galley." The signor looked up to the deck of the ship where Marco's father and uncle stood. "Your father wants you to come aboard now. He's waving to you, Marco."

All three clustered around Marco for the final good-by. Rosa's eyes were filled with tears. Signor Gilberto bent and kissed Marco on both cheeks. Even Christopher laid his lips shyly and briefly against Marco's face.

"Good-by, good-by, good-by!" they called as at last he ran toward the ship.

Rosa held her handkerchief to her eyes.

"Godspeed, Marco!" she cried. "Godspeed, my bambino!" She was thinking of him now as though he were a child again.

Halfway up the steps, Marco turned and waved.

Halfway up the steps, Marco turned and waved

"Good-by!" cried Christopher. "Come back to us safely!"

Marco was shaking with excitement as he climbed on up the steps. How wonderful it was to hear the galley slaves chanting an old song of the sea as they took up their oars! How wonderful to see the mainsail take the wind and veer gaily to the east.

To the east, thought Marco. Again he remembered places his father had mentioned since he had come home. Bagdad. Alexandria. Golden Kanbalu!

Messer Maffeo approached the boy as he reached the deck.

"We're on our way now, Marco," he said merrily. "We are on our way!"

The ship quivered and groaned as it began to move. The travelers stood at the stern and waved to their friends until Venice seemed but a speck against the bright blue sky.

Finally Marco's father said: "Let us go down below and settle ourselves in our cabins."

And so the thrilling voyage began. Day after day, as the sweating galley slaves rowed the big ship, Marco learned many new things. One afternoon, as they walked on the deck, he said

[31]

to his father: "I have always wanted a sea voyage, but I never really dreamed how pleasant one could be."

"This one is pleasant because we have had fair weather," his father replied. "But wait until we meet with a storm." Messer Nicolo looked at the blue horizon. "The wind and the weather are often great enemies. And there will be other moments of danger. Your uncle Maffeo and I have gone through many hardships on our way to and from Cathay."

Marco looked toward the east.

"I am almost seventeen, Father, and I'd be a great coward if I feared danger," he said.

Messer Nicolo seemed pleased at this.

"We will travel not only by sea where there is danger of pirates, but by caravan also, where there is danger from cutthroats and thieves. But once we have reached the outer borders of Cathay, we will have the Golden Tablet to protect us."

"The Golden Tablet?" Marco repeated. "You have never mentioned that before."

Messer Nicolo smiled. "Come down to my cabin. I will show it to you," he said.

Marco followed him wonderingly. What could the Golden Tablet be?

[*32*]

A sea chest stood in his father's cabin. Messer Nicolo unlocked it and took out a tablet made of pure gold. It was one foot long and three inches wide. Words were carved upon it in a language Marco could not understand.

"This tablet is a passport, Marco. It was given to me by the Great Khan himself." He thrust it into Marco's hands. "The words engraved upon it are in the Tartar language," he went on. "They mean that we are entitled to protection anywhere in the Great Khan's kingdom—that food, shelter, and even horses and guards will be given us."

Marco ran his hand along the tablet's shining surface.

"It is a wonderful thing," he murmured, "a most wonderful thing." Then he pleased his father again by saying, "But I hope we will not use it until we must. Signor Gilberto always says that a brave man likes to depend on the strength of his own hands."

Fair winds continued to blow the galley across the Adriatic Sea. Presently the day arrived when the ship put into port. Here the Polos left the galley to travel on by caravan. They would be traveling by land now, for many, many months.

Preparations for this part of the journey were made in a large field outside the gates of a strange city. It was thrilling for Marco to see a caravan being assembled there. He watched the tall, dark caravan master giving orders to his assistants. More than a score of armed horsemen were to make up the caravan, with extra horses to carry tents and baggage. There were also extra men to take care of the tents and horses, and to cook the food.

Marco and his father walked about the field, looking at everything. All at once Marco pointed to a gaily colored tent-wagon. It was like a little house set on a two-wheeled cart.

"What's that?" he asked.

"That is called a yurt, my son," Marco's father replied. "In our caravan this yurt will serve as a kitchen where some of the food will be prepared. Let me take you inside and show it to you."

Marco followed his father up some steps and through an opening at the rear of the yurt. When he stepped inside he found himself in a good-sized room.

In one part of the room there was a stone hearth on which a cooking-fire could be built. There was a table on which to work, and there were chests filled with good things to eat. An opening in the domelike roof provided for the escape of smoke.

"This is like the wagons I have seen gypsies ride in!" Marco exclaimed.

"That could be true," answered his father. "Roving tribes in ancient countries began to use such carts years ago." His fine eyes twinkled as he went on, "This one belongs strictly to the cook, who is a most important person in every caravan."

Marco followed his father out of the yurt, delighted. An assistant to the caravan master was waiting for them. His hand was on the bridle of a prancing mare. The mare's coat was white and glistened like silver in the sun.

"Oh, what a beautiful horse!" cried Marco.

The stocky man smiled. "She is a spirited Arabian," he said. "She can run like the wind." He thrust the bridle into Marco's hand. "She is yours, young Marco Polo. Her name is Shiraz and you are to ride her on our journey."

"Shiraz!" Marco repeated the name with joy.

He led the horse to a near-by palm tree, and gave her a date to win her affection. His bright eyes danced as she nuzzled against him.

[35]

"We'll be good companions," he said. "I can scarcely wait to start on our journey!"

The caravan master's assistant smiled.

"You won't have very long to wait. We leave tomorrow at sunrise."

At dawn, everything was ready. The entire caravan assembled and waited for the starting signal. Marco sat on Shiraz, looking very proud. Strangely enough, he was thinking of Christopher and wishing he were here to share this great moment. Behind him, also mounted, were his father and his uncle Maffeo. Behind them were the other horsemen.

It was exciting to watch the caravan master gallop up and down the line to see that all was well. He signaled to the outriders whom he had appointed to ride ahead of the caravan and to act as scouts.

The brow of a hill was bright with sunrise. As the caravan master finally galloped up to the head of the line, he and his horse were outlined against the rose-pearled sky. There was silence for a moment as the eyes of all the riders were focused upon him. Suddenly he lifted one arm very high. This was the starting signal! The horsemen all spoke a word to their horses. "Let's go, Shiraz!" Marco said gaily.

Shiraz tossed her head and started down the road. Some of the men began to sing strange songs of the desert. The caravan was on its way!

After many days, the travelers came to the flowery land of Persia. In province after province, Marco saw new faces, heard new sounds, and watched people who had many customs which were strange to him.

It was fun to travel by caravan. He liked the nights as well as the daytime hours. When evening came he helped to build the campfire. The men told stories as they sat around it, watching flames soar high.

Marco listened, fascinated, to the tale of the Caliphs of Bagdad. He heard about the fire

[37]

worshipers. But the most exciting tale of all was about the men of magic. It was said that they were a fearsome clan of robbers who had a strange power. They were able to create great fogs of dust to cover their attacks on travelers.

"Where are these men?" Marco asked the storyteller.

The old man looked grim. "We are in their region now and must be on the lookout for them. Be quick to draw your sword if they should appear. They are killers to a man. Natives call them the Karaunas."

"All this is true, my friends," the caravan master added. "The Karaunas are as evil a lot as any on the face of the earth."

Marco's eyes widened. He felt his heart beating hard. Would they meet the Karaunas in this strange country? Would these terrible men attack them? And what would he do in such a crisis, he wondered?

He, Marco Polo, now seventeen years old, would be expected to show his mettle!

CHAPTER FOUR

The Karaunas Attack

THE caravan was traveling through high and lonely mountains in Persia. Marco shivered with the cold.

His uncle Maffeo, riding beside him, teased: "Put on another coat, my lad! You are wearing only seven!"

"Is it always so cold in these mountains?" asked Marco.

"It's so cold that not many people can live here," answered his uncle. "That is why we have seen only cattle and herdsmen. Don't worry about it, though. We will soon be riding down into the valley. It will be so warm down there that you'll see apple trees in blossom."

"I'll like that!" laughed Marco.

He was about to urge Shiraz into a brisk trot when suddenly the caravan halted. The cara-

[*39*]

van master signaled to all the riders to pay attention.

"Men," he said soberly, "we are about to descend this mountain. The road will be treacherous. It leads through a narrow pass where danger lurks on every side. Watch out for crevices that may cripple your horses. Do not be alarmed by the beating of wings. They will be the wings of falcons for which this country is famous.

"I have told our scouts to ride ahead when we reach the plain below and to keep their eyes open for anything that looks like a dust storm. Such a thing might mean that the Karaunas are on their way to attack us."

"The Karaunas!" Every rider repeated the name with anxiety.

"On our way!" called the caravan master, and gave the starting signal by lifting one arm.

The mountain pass was narrow and made dark by overhanging trees. The travelers had to pick their way almost step by step. Crevices in the roadbed were filled with sharp stones. The beat of falcons' wings was frightening. These huge birds with reddish breasts disliked the sound of human beings passing through their native wilds.

Shiraz trembled with fear as one of the falcons swooped so low across the pass that it almost brushed her face with its wings.

"Steady, Shiraz! Steady!" Marco patted her head and dismounted. He took her bridle in his hand and led her gently along the road. Shadows of great boulders seemed to threaten them from both sides.

At last the descent was completed. The mountain pass lay behind the travelers and they found themselves on a vast plain. Here were many villages. As the caravan went on Marco could see that all of the villages were fortified with high walls made of mud.

He spoke to his father, who was riding beside him. "These people must be afraid of something. Look at those high walls!"

"They hope the walls will offer protection against the Karaunas," his father answered.

Marco looked ahead with watchful eyes. Suddenly he was startled by the sight of two scouts galloping furiously back to the caravan.

"The Karaunas are coming!" they shouted. "Turn back! Turn back!"

Far ahead of the caravan, Marco could see great clouds of dust rising from the plain. This was the "fog" the Karaunas made to cover their attacks. It made it impossible for riders to take aim at them until they had almost reached their victims. Quickly the fog came closer.

"Fight for your lives, men!" The caravan master cried savagely.

Marco felt his throat go dry. Shiraz was moving under the saddle as if she were on flying

[*42*]

feet. He must turn her back or he would be riding directly into the dreaded Karaunas! He drew on her reins sharply and Shiraz made a turn so complete that almost at once they were headed back toward the mountain pass.

"Good, Shiraz! Good!" He spoke to her gratefully.

"Marco! Marco!" His father was calling him from a spot several yards ahead.

"I am coming, Father," he answered.

He was about to rein in Shiraz beside his father's horse when suddenly there came the sound of blood-curdling cries:

"Karaunas! Karaunas! Karaunas!"

The Karaunas were already upon them, shouting their own name to terrify the caravan. Shiraz tossed her head and neighed shrilly.

"I don't see Maffeo, Marco." His father's voice was tense. "He was here a moment ago!"

The caravan was now in chaos. Men and horses were running about in every direction. Some were tearing across the plain like phantom men on phantom horses, followed by Karauna bandits riding hard. Just behind him, Marco heard the sound of steel clashing against steel as some of the Karaunas attacked the travelers with swords.

[*43*]

Marco turned Shiraz quickly around to face the oncoming bandits. He dug his spurs into her sides and rode toward the Karaunas.

"Marco!" his father called. "Come back! Come back!"

"I am going to find Uncle Maffeo!" Marco shouted over his shoulder.

Almost as he spoke the words, volleys of arrows were discharged around him. He was caught in the thick of the fray. He felt his heart pounding like a hammer as he heard the awful cries of men being slain on every side. He lost sight of his father, who had turned to follow him.

"That young one there!" a near-by Karauna cried. "Take him! Take him!"

"I will not be afraid! I will not!" Marco was talking wildly to himself as the bandit started after him.

Again he dug his spurs into Shiraz and rode on ahead of the Karauna. He hoped the bandit would not throw a knife into his back! He had heard that Karaunas were masters of the art of knife throwing!

"Uncle Maffeo!" he called as he galloped on. "Where are you? Uncle Maffeo!"

The Karauna was gaining upon him. Marco

attempted to guide his horse circle-wise around the bandit. Suddenly he heard his uncle's voice.

"Marco! Marco!"

Messer Maffeo came running from behind a high stone wall. Where was his horse, Marco wondered. Had it been shot out from under him?

Suddenly, as Marco had feared, the Karauna threw a knife—not at him—but at Maffeo. The Karauna shouted wildly as it missed its mark. Marco galloped to his uncle's side and slowed Shiraz down so that Maffeo could leap up on her back behind him.

"The Karaunas have killed our caravan master!" Maffeo gasped. "Ride on, Marco! Ride on!"

The Karauna had stopped to pick up his knife. Now he galloped after them. Suddenly Marco wheeled Shiraz around to face their pursuer.

"Marco! What are you doing?" His uncle Maffeo was aghast.

Marco's move surprised the Karauna. The man reined in his horse, looking suddenly puzzled. Quick as a flash, Marco drew a short sword from his girdle.

Marco took skillful aim and threw the sword

"I can try knife throwing too!" he said courageously to his uncle.

Almost as he spoke the words, Marco took skillful aim and threw the sword. An instant later the Karauna gave a terrible cry and toppled from his horse.

Maffeo hugged Marco with joy.

"Brave boy!" he cried. "You have saved our lives!"

The Karauna's black horse stood pawing the ground. Maffeo dismounted from Shiraz and ran to where the black horse stood. Before he took the animal's bridle, he examined the Karauna and found he was dead.

"You took wonderful aim, my boy," he called. "Your sword lies just below his heart."

Marco felt suddenly squeamish. He had had no desire to kill a man. But if he had not done so, he and Uncle Maffeo might both have lost their lives.

"Now shall we find my father?" he asked, eager to be gone from this place on the plain.

Uncle Maffeo answered: "We have come a long way from where the fight started. I do not think that we should go back. If Nicolo is alive, I think he would have the good sense to go to the Castle of Consolmi."

"Where's that?" asked Marco.

"It is not so far from here," answered Uncle Maffeo, "and the lord of the castle will give us shelter. We have talked with him at the court of the Great Khan." He mounted the Karauna's horse. "I will lead the way, Marco."

Marco followed his uncle with a heavy heart. He was thankful that they had escaped, but he was worried about his father. They had not gone more than a few miles, however, when to his great joy, his father appeared. He was waiting for them at a roadside well.

"Praise be to God!" he greeted them.

They lingered at the well and talked about the battle. "All the men in the caravan who were not killed," said Marco's father, "were bound with ropes to be sold as slaves."

Maffeo told Nicolo about how bravely Marco had attacked the bandit. Nicolo's words of praise were few, but he beamed with pride.

Hours later they approached the Castle of Consolmi. They crossed a bridge built over a moat. Moonlight shone on stone battlements. Marco could see silk banners flying from lofty turrets. He patted Shiraz with a loving hand.

"You were brave in battle, Shiraz. You helped me to win! I am thankful that you, too,

escaped. I should not like to be without you!"
A castle bell tolled from the bell tower.

There was the clang of heavy gates. The travelers rode into a spacious courtyard, grateful for the shelter of the Castle of Consolmi.

CHAPTER FIVE

Drums of the Desert

THE Polos rested at the Castle of Consolmi several days. On the morning they were ready to leave, the lord of the castle warned: "You will soon be crossing the Desert of Lop. It is a terrible place for travelers, because it is filled with evil spirits."

"What do they look like?" asked Marco.

"No living man has ever seen them," the lord of the castle replied slowly. "They are known only by the strange noises they make. They fill the air with the clash of arms or the beat of drums, and sometimes they even call out your name."

"How could they know what your name is —mine or yours—or anyone's?" Marco questioned again.

"It almost passes belief," answered the lord

[*50*]

of the castle, "but often they call a traveler or even his horse by name. They make their voices sound like someone's voice familiar to you—"

Messer Maffeo looked puzzled. "I don't understand this," he interrupted.

"Suppose," explained the lord of the castle, "that you are traveling by caravan on the desert and Marco, perhaps, has loitered behind you. If suddenly you were to hear him call, 'Uncle Maffeo!' wouldn't you answer his call at once?"

"Of course I would," said Maffeo.

"Suppose then," continued the lord of the castle, "that when you reached the spot where you thought his call had come from, Marco was not there. Wouldn't you try to search for him, especially if you heard his voice calling you again and again?"

"Without a doubt!" Maffeo exclaimed.

The lord of the castle looked grim.

"That would be your undoing," he said. "It would not have been Marco calling at all. It would have been the voice of evil spirits. They would be trying to lure you away from the protection of the caravan to a lonely death."

While attendants brought the Polos' horses

into the courtyard, Marco asked the lord of the castle another question.

"Do these spirits make warlike attacks like the Karaunas?"

"Only phantom attacks," the lord of the castle answered.

"Phantom attacks?" repeated Marco. "What are they?"

The lord of the castle fondled Shiraz as he explained.

"Travelers have seen what appeared to be a body of armed men advancing toward them. In fear of being attacked, they have taken flight. They are thus led off the right path and lost. No living mortals ever attack them, but they are terrified by strange sounds, and they starve to death on the desert."

Marco's father mounted his horse with a sober look. "We will beware of the Desert of Lop," he told the lord of the castle. "Thank you for warning us of its danger."

Marco and Maffeo mounted their horses also. They thanked the lord of the castle warmly for the happy time they had spent with him. Marco's father leaned from his saddle and put his hand on the lord of the castle's shoulder.

"Peace be with you here," he said.

"And peace be with you on your way," said
the lord of the castle with a gesture of farewell.

The castle bell tolled three times. This was
a signal to let down the drawbridge so the travelers could ride across the moat. Marco galloped across the bridge, leaving his father and
uncle to ride more slowly behind. He waved
to them gaily.

"I'll race you to the first well!" he called. "This is a bright morning and we should make the most of it!"

They laid a light whip on their horses and cantered after him down the road.

The Polos were to join another organized caravan when they came to the edge of the desert. Marco's father had not told him that in this particular caravan he would ride a camel instead of riding Shiraz.

On the day the caravan was sighted, Marco reined in his horse with excitement.

"Look, Father!" he cried. "Our caravan has camels in it!"

Messer Nicolo laughed.

"I knew it would have camels, son, but I wanted to surprise you! You will be riding a camel across the desert. Shiraz and the other horses will be brought along, but we will ride on camels because they travel better on sand and require little water and food."

A cameleer gave Marco a fawn-colored camel to ride. It looked like a lumpy creature with its two large humps. After riding a horse with the grace of Shiraz, the camel seemed very ungainly, but Marco climbed up on her back, determined to ride her well.

"She should be fun to ride," he said to his uncle Maffeo, "after I get used to her."

Maffeo shrugged his shoulders.

"Many camels are spiteful creatures and spit at you when they are surly," he said.

Marco stroked the camel's bony head.

"I shall try to be good friends with this one," he told his uncle. Then he asked the cameleer, "What is her name?"

"She is called Balishan," answered the cameleer, "because she came from Balishan. The finest rubies in the world are mined in that province. She was used as a cargo camel to carry the rubies from the mines."

"Balishan," repeated Marco. "It is a good name, I think."

After a night's rest in the town of Lop on the edge of the desert, the caravan was ready to leave. Each man and beast stood in his appointed place, awaiting the caravan master's signal. Finally he galloped up to the head of the camel train. He lifted one arm high as the sun rose in the sky. The caravan was on the march!

Marco's father rode behind him.

"How do you like riding a camel?" he called to Marco.

"Balishan is fine," answered Marco, "but she rocks like a ship on the high seas. No wonder they call a camel the ship of the desert." A moment later, he added, "I only hope that Shiraz doesn't mind walking on this sand."

Marco's father looked back to the rear of the caravan.

"She's plodding along very well," he told Marco. "She will travel more easily without your weight on her back."

The sandy desert stretched before them, mile after weary mile. They would have to travel thirty days to cross it. At the end of each day's march, they planned to stop at a place where they could get water.

At the beginning of the third day's journey, Marco was reminded of the lord of the Castle of Consolmi when the caravan master said: "We are now upon that part of the desert where the evil spirits dwell. Remember to stay together, men. Don't let the spirits lure you away from the protection of this caravan. If you think you hear your name being called, be sure to make no answer."

The caravan set out. But the travelers had scarcely gone a mile when Marco heard strange noises. At first they sounded like far-off music, then like the beating of drums. Rata-tat-tat. Rata-tat-tat. Bong! Bong! Bong!

"Pay no attention to them, men!" ordered the caravan master. "Look straight ahead and keep riding on!"

Suddenly there came the sound of a rushing wind. It was wild and uncanny. Marco huddled closer to the friendly protection of Balishan's hump. Again the wind blew, seeming to stir up clouds of yellow sand as if it were beginning to storm. Suddenly Marco sat erect, a terrified look in his eyes.

The wind was calling the name of his horse! *"Shiraz! Shiraz! Shiraz!"*

"Father!" Marco cried. "It's—" Then suddenly he was silent because he saw an astounding thing.

Shiraz had broken out of the line of horses in the rear. She was running helter-skelter across the hard-baked sands.

"Shiraz!" Marco cried out loudly.

The little mare paused and looked around with bewildered eyes. Again the wind blew crazily, seeming to call her name. She tossed her head, and with flying mane, started running away from the caravan.

"Shiraz!" Marco guided Balishan out of the

[57]

The wind was calling the name of his horse!

line of camels and tore off across the sands in pursuit.

"Marco!" His father's voice was fearful. "Come back! Come back! *Marco!*"

The caravan master ordered the caravan to halt. As the bleak wind continued to cry, *"Shiraz! Shiraz! Shiraz!"* he called on the scouts to ride after Marco.

"Patience!" the caravan master said to Marco's frantic father. "These scouts will bring him back!"

Marco was riding fast after Shiraz. He could hear the scouts following him, but he was determined to bring Shiraz out from under the spell of the evil spirits. He paid no heed to the camel riders behind him.

"Shiraz!" he cried. "Stand still! Stand still!"

Shiraz paused again, looking around wild-eyed. Marco was about to get off his camel and race to her side when suddenly a loop of rope dropped over his head and was pulled tight around his waist.

One cameleer had captured him. Another had captured Shiraz. They rode up to his side as the angry wind sobbed on and on. One of the scouts loosened the rope around his waist.

"You had a narrow escape!" he exclaimed.

"So has Shiraz," said Marco, "and we thank you both from our hearts. It's lucky for us that you are skilled in throwing ropes!"

And so the dangerous trip continued. Day after day, the air was filled with ghostly sounds.

And day after day, the riders rode on, trying to seem unaware of the evil spirits that sought to prey upon them.

At last the sinister Desert of Lop lay behind them.

"I am glad that part of the trip is over," Marco said to his father.

Messer Nicolo smiled.

"One takes many risks in traveling in strange countries," he said. "How do we know what may happen next?"

[60]

CHAPTER SIX

The Great Kublai Khan

THE travelers were riding through fertile country. Messer Maffeo pointed to the gilded roofs of a beautiful building a short distance ahead.

"There it is, Marco!" he said, reining in his horse. "The post house on the Purple River!"

Marco looked at a whole group of buildings. They were built on land that gently sloped down to the edge of a winding river. "It looks like a busy place!" he exclaimed. "But why do they call the river purple?"

His uncle Maffeo called his attention to flowering trees along the shore. "Those are wistaria trees in blossom. When their purple flowers blow into the river they give the water a purple glow and it is a lovely thing to see."

Marco shaded his eyes from the sun.

[*61*]

"Cathay has beautiful trees and flowers," he said. "And its gardens, I think, are even more beautiful than those we have in Italy."

His father cantered up beside him.

"How do you like the post house, Marco?" he asked.

Marco laughed merrily, saying: "It looks as busy as the Grand Canal!"

"Sometimes it is more so," smiled his father. "And it is only one of ten thousand post houses! They were built by the Great Khan to increase speed in delivering royal messages to and from every part of his kingdom."

"Ten thousand post houses!" Marco gasped.

Messer Nicolo explained: "You will find one on every important highway leading out from Kanbalu. They are built twenty-five or thirty miles apart, and they are furnished as richly as a king's palace. Each one has four hundred fine horses kept in constant readiness for the use of royal messengers."

"Are we going to stop at this post house?" asked Marco.

"Indeed we are," said his father. "We will rest here several days before we begin the last lap of our journey."

"I will like stopping here," said Marco.

He spoke to Shiraz and she galloped on ahead of his companions.

The Polos needed time to rest. It was three and a half years since they had sailed from Venice. Just before they reached the border of Cathay Marco had become very ill. For a year he had been too sick to travel. That time had not been wholly lost, however, because he had begun to learn the Mongol language as soon as he became strong enough to talk.

Now as they were crossing Cathay, he was able to speak to the native people and to make them understand him.

Suddenly Marco brought Shiraz to a stop. In front of him on the road leading directly to the post house, two young boys were quarreling. Their fists flew and they tore at one another's hair.

"Ai ya! Ai ya!" one of them shrieked. "Be careful or I will kill you! You son of a talking parrot!"

"What seems to be the trouble, boys?" Marco smiled down from his horse.

The older one scowled.

"This midget wants to be a post rider!" he exclaimed. "He is jealous because I am allowed to ride a horse when I serve the Great Khan."

He put his hand over the younger boy's mouth as he started to speak, then added scornfully, "He is only a foot-messenger!"

"And what is a foot-messenger?" asked Marco, wishing to learn the ways of this system.

"Who wants to know?" cried the younger boy, breaking away from the older one.

"I do," said Marco pleasantly.

"And what is your name?" the small boy bellowed. "Your face is white and you are so tall that you could be a walking giant! You do not belong to this country, do you?"

The boy was so angry that he looked comical. Like all foot-messengers in the Great Khan's kingdom, he wore a red girdle around his waist. There were several small bells attached to it. As he ran from post station to post station, all these bells would ring to call attention to his coming.

Now, because he was angry and shaking himself like a duck, the bells were ringing merrily. Marco burst into laughter.

"My name is Marco Polo," he said, in answer to the boy's question. "And I come from a country across the sea."

The taller boy slapped the younger one hard.

"It is not for you, Chen Fu," he said, "to talk like this to a stranger! This man looks handsome and wise. He is of noble lineage, I am sure. Look at his rich clothing! Look at his fine horse! Now tell him you are sorry for your bad manners!"

Chen Fu looked suddenly defeated. He had the grace to feel ashamed as he looked up at Marco's smiling face again.

"I am sorry, Walking Giant!" Suddenly he smiled. "And, believe me, I am not jealous of this son of a pompous donkey! It is just that I have earned the right to be a post rider and have not yet been given a horse." He put out his hand almost shyly and fondled the velvety nose of Shiraz. "This is a good horse, Walking Giant! A very good horse!"

There was something about the boy's droll face that made Marco like him. He also liked his fighting spirit and noted that he handled Shiraz with very gentle hands.

"I think that you love horses," Marco said to Chen Fu, "and that is really why you want to be a post rider."

Chen Fu looked sad.

"I have wanted a horse all my life," he said as he nuzzled Shiraz against him. "Sometimes I think that I can no longer wait."

Marco leaned down from his saddle and put his hand on the boy's dark head.

"Shiraz could use a new attendant," he said kindly. "The groom who now takes care of her wishes to stay in his native village instead of going on to Kanbalu." Marco smiled as Chen Fu fastened large dark eyes upon him. "Would you like to take care of Shiraz, Chen Fu, and go with me wherever I must go?"

Chen Fu was so overcome that he knelt and bowed his head to the ground.

"O Honorable Walking Giant!" he exclaimed, "I would be so happy—"

The other boy looked annoyed.

"Do not call Marco Polo 'Walking Giant'!" he scolded. "Call him the Honorable Marco Polo!"

Marco laughed gaily.

"But I like to be called Walking Giant!" He leaned down and spoke again to Chen Fu. "Take my horse's bridle and lead her to the post-house steps where my father is waiting."

Chen Fu took the bridle happily. He would not have been funny little Chen Fu if he had not looked triumphantly at the post rider as he walked away.

There were many people coming and going at this busy post house. Mandarins in brocaded robes went soberly about their business. Lords from the Great Khan's court and officers of rank, all splendidly arrayed, came and went in great numbers.

Boys who were proud to be post riders galloped to and fro on their spirited horses. A dozen foot-messengers like Chen Fu ran hither and thither while all the bells on their girdles rang, making gay sounds.

"I see you have a new companion," said Marco's father as Chen Fu led Shiraz up to the post-house steps.

"This is Chen Fu," said Marco gaily. "He is going to be my new groomsman."

"Good!" laughed Marco's father.

He got off his horse and followed Marco and Uncle Maffeo into the big post house.

As soon as the Polos arrived at the post house, the news of their coming was taken to the Great Khan at his summer palace forty miles away. He was so pleased to learn that the Polos had reached Cathay that he sent a special escort to conduct them to Shangtu.

"You will like Shangtu," Chen Fu told Marco. "The palace is built of marble and there is a beautiful park around it. There are also the royal meadows where the Great Khan keeps up a stud of ten thousand horses and mares which are as white as snow. These are so sacred to the Emperor that no one is allowed to place himself before them or to check their movements in any way."

"Ten thousand horses and mares—all as white as snow!" exclaimed Marco. "Can this really be true?"

Chen Fu nodded soberly. "It is true, Walking Giant," he answered. "The Great Khan has many wonderful things. And wait until you see *him!*"

Soon the Polos went on to Shangtu. And the day came when Marco and his father and his uncle Maffeo were to be received by the Great Khan.

The illustrious Kublai Khan sat in a gilded

Ahmad spoke in a low voice to the Khan

room on a golden chair inlaid with precious stones. He was dressed in a silken robe of state embroidered with rubies and pearls. The principal officers of his court stood around him. Ahmad, his favorite minister, was closest to his chair.

Silver trumpets were blown as the Polos were escorted down the length of the room. Their names were announced by a young officer.

"Into your gracious presence, O Great Kublai Khan," he said, "we bring your old friends, Messer Nicolo and Messer Maffeo Polo."

The brothers prostrated themselves full length on the floor before the Emperor. Marco waited quietly until they were recognized.

"Rise and know you are welcome," ordered the Great Khan. Then he looked kindly at Marco. "And who is this young man?"

Marco's father drew him forward. "This is your servant and my son," he said with pride.

Marco also prostrated himself before the Emperor. The Great Kublai Khan looked pleased.

"He is welcome," he said to Marco's father. "It pleases me much that you have brought him." He studied Marco with shrewd eyes. "He is a fine-looking young man and shall be enrolled among my attendants of honor."

All three Polos bowed to the floor while Marco's father said: "Receive our deepest thanks, O Kublai Khan!"

Meanwhile, Ahmad, the king's favorite minister, spoke in a low voice to the Khan. The Khan looked hesitant for a moment.

"No," he said to Ahmad, "I shall be pleased in this. Marco Polo shall be one of my attendants of honor." He looked at Marco again. Then he added, "Rise now, my honorable subjects from across the sea, and tell me about your travels."

Messer Nicolo acted as spokesman, and told the Great Khan about their journey from Venice to his golden court.

Marco listened quietly. He did not feel very quiet inside. He kept wondering why the king's minister had spoken about him to the Great Khan. From what the Khan had said in reply, Marco felt that Ahmad had objected because the Emperor had made him an attendant of honor.

"This man Ahmad doesn't like me," Marco said to himself. "And I must find out why."

Presently their audience with the Great Khan was over. Ahmad kept his eyes upon Marco as the Polos bowed themselves out of the room.

"I must be on my guard against him," thought Marco. "Yes, I must always be on my guard!"

CHAPTER SEVEN

Ahmad at Work

SOON the Polos were established at the
Great Khan's court. Marco continued to study
the language of the country, which was very
hard to learn.

Because he lived at the royal court, he
dressed as a young courtier. He wore the long
mandarin-like robes of the Chinese officials.
They were made of rich silk and wool and
embroidered with gold and silver threads.
And, because he was older now, he was known
as Marco Polo, the Noble Venetian.

One morning he and Chen Fu were walking
across the park toward the royal meadows.
Chen Fu ran ahead.

"Walking Giant! Oh, Walking Giant!" he
called over his shoulder. "Look! The snow-
white mares are in pasture!"

Marco shaded his eyes from the sun, then he stood quite still.

"This is a sight to behold!" he cried. "There must be thousands of them! And look, Chen Fu, they're running in herds!"

Chen Fu was delighted with his master's enthusiasm. "I told you there are ten thousand mares!" he exclaimed. "Look how fast they can run! Their hoofs are small and they shine like silver!"

Marco stood still, fascinated by the scene. Thousands of graceful white horses with coats even whiter than that of Shiraz tore across the wide green pastures toward a clear-flowing stream.

"They feel very gay this morning!" Marco said to Chen Fu. "See how they arch their beautiful necks and how high they carry their tails!"

"They are royal mares, Walking Giant," Chen Fu said, as if this told the whole story.

He raced up to a moon gate, which was a large round gate set in a stone wall, and leaned upon it, waiting for Marco to catch up with him.

"Is this as far as we are allowed to go, Chen Fu?" Marco asked.

Chen Fu nodded solemnly.

"Only the Great Khan goes in and out of this gate," he said. "It is his royal order that no one—no one, mind you, Walking Giant— is permitted to disturb these mares in pasture. Even the men who take care of them are watched by armed guards."

Marco looked beyond the moon gate.

"I see no guards here now," he said.

"You don't see them, but they are here," Chen Fu said wisely. "If you try to open this gate they will appear from nowhere!"

"I don't think I'll try," Marco laughed.

They watched the snow-white mares rush down to the edge of the river. Many raced into the water, and there was great splashing as they frolicked about.

Suddenly Marco and Chen Fu were startled as a child's voice cried out in great terror, "Help! Help! Oh, help!"

Turning quickly, Marco saw a little girl about a hundred feet away, huddled fearfully against the wall. She was staring wide-eyed at a cobra.

The large speckled snake was almost six feet long. It was not far from the child and it was ready to strike. Its angry head was raised and about a third of its body was swollen, as all cobras' bodies are, when they are ready to bite.

Marco lost no time. He picked up a big stone from a pile that lay along the wall. Running forward, he hurled it at the serpent. The little girl sobbed aloud as the snake gave an angry gasp and lay crushed at her feet.

"You had a narrow escape," Marco said kindly, as he lifted the child in his arms. He swung her high above the serpent, then stood her on her feet. "I am glad that we were here to help. Now, tell us, what is your name?"

[77]

Marco picked up a big stone

The little girl folded her small hands and bowed.

"My name is Mulan, Honorable Stranger," she said softly. "And I am ten years old."

Suddenly she flung herself face downward on the grass and sobbed.

"Here! Here!" cried Marco. "You must not cry now! The cobra is dead."

"I—I—am not crying now about the cobra," Mulan said as her tears kept falling. "And you were good, O Honorable Stranger, very good, to save my life!"

Marco tried to make her feel more cheerful.

"I would be a poor wretch, indeed, if I could not rescue one poor little girl from a big bad cobra!" he said teasingly. Then he picked her up. Taking a silk handkerchief from the pocket of his robe, he gently wiped away her tears. "I think that we shall be good friends if you will only tell me what else makes you cry."

Suddenly Mulan broke away from him.

"But I can't tell you now!" she cried. "I am on my way to the Great Khan's palace and I must get there in a hurry!"

Marco caught her by the hand. "Why must you go to the palace?" he asked.

[79]

Mulan sank to her knees before him.

"Please, O Honorable Stranger, let me go!" she begged. "Let me go! My honorable father is to be put on trial today for stealing!" Her big brown eyes were filled with misery. "He did not steal, I tell you! The Emperor's minister says he stole an emerald from a mandarin's robe, but that is not true! That is not true!"

Still holding Mulan's hand, Marco turned to Chen Fu. "Are there trials to be held at the palace today?" he asked.

Chen Fu answered quickly. "Yes, Walking Giant. Today is Ahmad's trial day at the Court of Thieves."

Marco turned back to Mulan.

"You say your father is innocent, but how do you know?" he asked.

Mulan thrust her hand into the pocket of her cotton coolie coat. She brought forth a clear green stone the color of an ocean wave.

"I have the emerald, Honorable Stranger," she said. "It was given to me by my father's brother who has fled from this country. He said if I would return it to Ahmad, it would save my father's life."

Marco made no answer. He gathered Mulan

into his arms and swung her up on to his shoulder.

"Let us make great haste," he said. "I have long legs and will carry you to the palace."

"I will run on ahead," cried Chen Fu, "and tell the court that you are coming."

The Court of Thieves was an unhappy place. Prisoners were brought before Ahmad, who showed them little courtesy and no mercy at all. Often he gave no justice when justice should have been given.

Today the courtroom was crowded. Many, many prisoners had already been sentenced to death. Their wild cries could be heard as they were dragged away from the courtroom.

Marco hurried into the courtroom with little Mulan on his shoulder. He was so much taller than the men of China that he towered above all the others. Ahmad saw him coming. He gave a start of surprise, then he spoke coldly. "Greetings, Noble Venetian! What brings you to the Court of Thieves?"

Marco hastened to stand before him.

"This child is Mulan," he said, setting the little girl on her feet. "She can prove the innocence of her honorable father! I ask, O Ahmad, that justice be given her."

Ahmad looked displeased.

"What is your father's name?" he asked frightened little Mulan.

"My honorable father's name is Chang Wang. He works in the kitchen of this palace."

"Chang Wang," repeated Ahmad. "Let me look at the record."

He looked through a sheaf of rice paper files that lay before him on his desk. Suddenly he smiled an evil smile.

"You have come too late," he said. "Your honorable father was given the death sentence. He has already been shot by the guards."

Marco could feel Mulan trembling all over, but he was not prepared for her suddenly angry words.

"My honorable father must have told

[*83*]

you that he was innocent!" she cried. "He did! I know he did! You are an evil minister! You put innocent people to death!"

Ahmad stood up in great wrath. The prisoners in the courtroom had begun to cheer for Mulan. Above the noise, Ahmad shouted: "Take her away! Take her away or I shall have her whipped!"

Marco led Mulan out of the room. She had said for him what he wanted to say. Her father had been innocent but he had been put to death. And he was only one of many!

Marco made a vow to himself. He would work against Ahmad in every way he could even if the minister *was* the favorite of the Great Khan.

CHAPTER EIGHT

On the Street of Singing Stars

Marco led Mulan away from the Court of Thieves. Chen Fu followed eagerly. When they came to a quiet place in a marble hall of the palace, Mulan turned to Marco.

"You were kind to me, Honorable Stranger," she said, bowing before him, "and I thank you more than words can tell." She held out one of her hands, opening it to show the emerald. "I will leave this in your keeping to return to Ahmad."

Marco took the emerald.

"I will give it back to him," he said grimly. "It ought to remind him of the great injustice he has done today. It will be up to him to return it to the mandarin from whom it was stolen."

Mulan watched Marco tuck the precious

stone into a white leather pouch he wore at his waist. Chen Fu spoke sympathetically.

"Where are you going now, Mulan?"

"I don't know where to go, Chen Fu," Mulan answered sadly. "My honorable mother worked too hard in the kitchen gardens and died, and now my honorable father is gone." She drew the little collar of her coolie coat up around her throat as if she were cold. "If I wander about the streets someone will pick me up and sell me as a slave," she added.

Suddenly she knelt before Marco Polo. "O Honorable Stranger!" she cried. "A slave girl's life is very hard! I do not want to be sold as a slave!"

Marco took her hands and raised her to her feet. "I will not let anyone sell you, Mulan," he said kindly. "Are you not skilled in work of any kind? Is there not something you can do?"

"My mother taught me to work on gauze and I know how to embroider well," Mulan said softly.

Marco's face lighted. He smiled down at her and again took her hand. "I know what to do now!" he exclaimed. "Come with me."

"But where are we going?" she asked in wonder as they started walking.

[86]

Marco looked happy. "We are going to see a princess!" he said.

"A—a princess!" Mulan was wide-eyed.

"Yes, I am going to take you to see the Princess of a Thousand Petticoats! They call her that because she has so many dresses and needs so many petticoats to go with them! Surely she could use a little worker on gauze!"

Chen Fu was delighted.

"Wonderful, Walking Giant! Oh, wonderful! Now that that is settled," he said, "I can go back to the royal stables!"

Marco found the Princess of a Thousand Petticoats in her royal sewing room. She was telling her needleworkers that she wanted white chrysanthemums embroidered on a blue satin gown.

Their hands flew like butterflies over beautiful materials. Much to Mulan's delight, there was a sewing table upon which lay yards and yards of gauze like pink clouds.

"Good morning, Princess." Marco bowed before the princess.

Then, for the first time, Mulan heard Marco's name.

"Good morning, Honorable Marco Polo," the princess said, and smiled. "What mission brings you to this place of chattering females?"

"I have brought you another female," said Marco. "I hope you will let her work for you."

"This little girl!" exclaimed the princess.

"This little girl," repeated Marco. "Her name is Mulan."

When the princess had heard Mulan's sad story, she spoke kindly.

"Leave her with me, Honorable Marco Polo," she said, and her hands fluttered toward Mulan like flowers. "I have a thousand yards of gauze to be embroidered!"

Marco looked down at Mulan. "Would you like to sew for this beautiful princess?" he asked.

Mulan bowed to the floor.

"I am so happy, Honorable Marco Polo," she said, smiling. "I am so very happy!"

The summer days went swiftly by. When the heat of the season was over, the Great Khan announced that he would move his court to his winter palace at Kanbalu.

"I shall be glad to go to the city," Marco told his father. "I think that Kanbalu will be a most interesting place."

Messer Nicolo answered him soberly.

"I hope you will see more of Kanbalu than you have seen of many things here. You are studying too hard. It is hard enough to master the Mongol language, but you are learning Arabic and Chinese at the same time!"

Marco laughed at his father's concern.

"If I do not learn to speak with the people who live in the Orient, I shall not be able to serve the Great Khan!"

Marco had to study hard for two long years to train himself to be of further use in the Great Khan's service. Meanwhile, affairs at the palace moved on.

Ahmad, the Khan's favorite minister, continued to treat the people unjustly. Although many people complained about him to the Great Khan, the Emperor still granted him favor after favor. People began to say that Ahmad used magic to paralyze the Great Khan's will.

One spring day in Kanbalu, Marco Polo was called before the Great Khan. After he had made his ceremonial bow, the Great Khan said, "You have studied long and well, young Marco Polo. I have learned that you are skilled in the speaking of many languages. I also note that you observe things well."

Marco made another bow. "Your attention pleases me much, O Great Khan," he said.

The Emperor raised his hand with a royal gesture.

"I am appointing you now to an important position in my service," he announced. "You are to be a Commissioner attached to my own Privy Council. I count on you to serve me wisely."

Marco was glad he was finding favor in the Great Khan's sight. Even Ahmad had not been able to prevent the Emperor from giving him this high position at his court.

He liked to walk on Theater Street

Marco delighted in walking the streets of Kanbalu. In this way, more than any other, he could study the customs of the people.

He liked to walk on Theater Street where lovely little actresses with painted lips and lacquered hair danced on outdoor stages. He walked through the Lane of the Ivory Carvers, too.

Sometimes he strolled along the Street of the Astrologers. More than five thousand astronomers worked in high and beautiful observatories on this street. They had marvelous equipment made out of bronze and beaten gold. They studied the way of the stars and could forecast things to come. Even the Great Khan never started upon a journey unless these astrologers set a favorable time for him to go.

It was on this Street of Singing Stars, as it was sometimes called, that Marco Polo met with a strange adventure. He was standing in the entrance to one of the observatories, waiting for Chen Fu to come along with Shiraz, so that he might ride back to the palace.

Night had almost fallen and the street was shadowy. Suddenly he heard voices behind him.

"This is the hour!" one voice was saying. "It is written in the stars that we should strike our enemy tonight!"

Two young men were standing halfway up the stairs that led to the observatory. Marco felt sure that they had been talking with an astrologer who had told them that this was a favorable time to do whatever they had planned.

"It is written in the stars," one of them had said.

"Who is the enemy they plan to strike?" Marco Polo wondered. "And what do they plan to do?"

He hid himself behind the door that led into the street. He flattened himself against the wall as they came down the stairs and paused for a moment in the entrance. They were so close to him that he might have touched them.

"Shall we go directly to the palace?" one young man asked.

"Let us lose no time!" the other said excitedly.

Marco decided to wait no longer for Chen Fu. He would follow these men and try to learn their mission. Did their enemy live at the palace? Could it be someone he knew?

The men started walking down the Street of Singing Stars at a rapid pace. Stealthily, Marco followed them.

CHAPTER NINE

Murder in the Palace

THE men walked on until they came to the marble wall surrounding the palace. They paused at a sign from a guard who stood at the main entrance gate.

Marco stepped back into the shadow of a flowering Ming tree. Would the guard do his duty and question them, he wondered, or would he let them pass?

Much to Marco's surprise, the guard greeted them by name.

"Good evening, Wang Chu," he said. "Good evening, Chang-i."

They answered him pleasantly. He opened the gate for them to pass through. Marco spoke from the shadows. "Good evening, guard," he said.

The guard was a bit startled as Marco

stepped forward. Then he recognized him.

"Oh, it is you, the Noble Venetian!" he said. "I did not see you coming."

Marco looked at him inquiringly.

"Those men you allowed to pass through the gate," he asked, "do you know them?"

"They are attached to the staff of Prince Chingkam, Honorable Sir. They have worked in the palace for years!"

Marco felt sure that the guard was telling the truth.

"There are so many thousands of people at

the palace," Marco said, "I suppose it will be years until I recognize them all!"

"It will not be years," laughed the guard, "until they recognize you! The Noble Venetian is already known throughout Kanbalu!"

"Good night, guard," said Marco, as he passed through the gate. "May you have the luck of a Pink Salamander!"

Marco walked across the inner courtyard to the jeweled entrance of the palace. He decided to forget about the men he had followed. If they were trusted employees of Prince Chingkam, he felt he had no right to interfere in their affairs.

Marco meant to spend the evening writing out some reports for the Great Khan. The Emperor had gone away to hunt in the forests of Shangtu. Prince Chingkam had accompanied him. Marco wanted to have these reports ready when they came back to Kanbalu.

It was almost midnight when he heard a low knock on his door. He was sitting in an ebony chair at a pearl-incrusted table. He looked up, startled. Who could be calling upon him at so late an hour? Again that soft knocking. Marco went to the door and opened it. Chen Fu stood there, bowing.

"Chen Fu!" exclaimed Marco. "Why—?"

"Please, Walking Giant!" interrupted Chen Fu, laying his fingers against his lips.

Marco motioned him to come into the room. As soon as he had crossed the threshold, Chen Fu closed the door.

"Now tell me why you are here," said Marco.

[*98*]

Chen Fu was breathing hard.

"I had a hard time getting here," he said, puffing for breath. "Guards are everywhere at night!"

"Of course they are," said Marco. "Isn't that as it should be? Why are you abroad?"

Chen Fu explained why he had come. "I was coming back from the royal stables. I had left my cap in Shiraz's stall. I knew that it was very late, but I could not sleep."

"Go on," said Marco, as Chen Fu paused.

"I was trying to dodge the Captain of the Imperial Guard on duty at the inner palace gate when I saw Ahmad—"

"Ahmad!" echoed Marco, amazed. "Why should he be at the gate at midnight? He does not live at the palace!"

Chen Fu nodded his head. "I heard the captain ask him why and Ahmad told him that the prince had sent for him."

Marco began pacing up and down the room.

"But Prince Chingkam went hunting with the Great Khan!" he told Chen Fu.

"So the captain told Ahmad," Chen Fu replied. "But Ahmad said that the prince had come back and wanted to see him at once. It must be something urgent, he said, or he would not have sent for him in the middle of the night! After a little more talk, the captain let him pass."

"But I am sure that the prince is away!" Marco exclaimed. Suddenly, remembering the men he had followed on the Street of Singing Stars, he seized Chen Fu by the arm. "All is not well here tonight, Chen Fu! Come, we will talk to the Captain of the Guard!"

They hurried out of the room and down the marble hall.

Suddenly a strong voice called, "Halt, man and boy! Halt!"

Marco turned around to face the captain he was seeking.

"Oh, it is you, Noble Venetian!" the captain said hastily.

"Yes, it is I," said Marco. "My boy, Chen Fu, saw the king's minister at the gate. He tells me that Ahmad had a message from Prince Chingkam. I know for a fact that the prince is with the Great Khan at Shangtu! Something is wrong, Captain."

"Come with me!" exclaimed the captain. "I, too, fear foul play!"

Several soldiers armed with strong bows and arrows joined the captain, who led the way to

Prince Chingkam's apartment. The captain opened the door quietly and halted on the threshold.

The men behind him looked into the room and saw a man seated on a silken dais. In the flickering candlelight, even Marco Polo took him to be Prince Chingkam.

"He must have returned to the palace without the knowledge of anyone!" Marco thought, puzzled. He stared at Ahmad, who was kneeling on the floor, waiting to be addressed by His Royal Highness.

At that moment a man came out of the shadows beyond the circle of candlelight. Because of the dim light, Marco could not see that he was Chang-i, one of the men he had followed from the Street of Singing Stars. He was carrying a long curved sword. Quickly he moved up behind the minister, who was still kneeling on the floor. He lifted the sword high and with one stroke, he cut off Ahmad's head.

Chen Fu uttered a terrified cry. Marco Polo gasped aloud. So quickly had the terrible deed been done that even the Captain of the Imperial Guard could not have crossed the room in time to prevent it.

Now, with a cry of fury, the captain raised

The captain's men seized Chang-i and dragged him away

his bow and loosed an arrow. It missed Chang-i but it killed the man on the dais. Meanwhile, the captain's men seized Chang-i, the murderer, and dragged him away.

The captain turned to Marco.

"The man on the dais was not Prince Chingkam," he told him. "I saw that almost at once. He must have been a friend of Chang-i's who helped him in this plot against Ahmad."

Marco looked at the lifeless one slumped upon the throne. Suddenly he recognized him as the second man he had seen on the Street of Singing Stars.

"He was a friend of Chang-i's, all right," he said grimly. "I saw them both together earlier this evening."

Marco looked away from the hideous sight of Ahmad's headless body.

"They must have been planning this deed for months," said the captain. "The Great Khan will see that Chang-i is punished."

When daylight came, Marco sought his father. He told him what had happened in the middle of the night. Messer Nicolo was shocked. "The Great Khan will be furious," he said. "He will see that justice is done!"

Marco surprised him by saying: "Why

should the Great Khan punish Chang-i for killing such a man as Ahmad? Ahmad was an evil minister. He was hated throughout Cathay. He gave no justice to anyone, not even to little Mulan."

Suddenly he began to pace up and down.

"Now that I have had time to think about this," he said, "I feel sure that Chang-i and Wang Chu were real patriots. When they killed Ahmad they did a good deed for the country. It would not be right for the Great Khan to punish Chang-i, and I intend to tell him so."

"Marco!" His father looked at him in amazement. "No one tells the Great Khan what is right and what is not right."

"I shall, Father," Marco said firmly. "If Ahmad had not been killed, the people might have revolted against the Great Khan some day. When the Khan returns to the palace I am going to tell him this."

"I beg of you not to," his father cried. "You are in the Great Khan's favor. But Ahmad was his favorite minister. If you speak against Ahmad and stand up for Chang-i, the Khan may dismiss you from his court. Promise me that you will have nothing to do with this matter."

But Marco would not make such a promise. When the Great Khan returned to the palace, Marco appeared before him. He told the Khan that he knew the people would be glad to hear that Ahmad was dead. He told how they had hated the minister, and had believed Ahmad used magic to paralyze the good Khan's will.

He told how the Khan's people were ready to revolt because Ahmad had sentenced so many innocent men to death. And he begged that Chang-i should not be punished for his part in the plot against the minister.

When Marco had finished, the Great Khan looked at him in silence. Marco thought he was angry and ready to punish him for daring to speak in such a fashion. Finally the Great Khan nodded gravely.

"You are a brave man, Messer Marco Polo!" he said. "You have opened my eyes to grievous things. I shall see that from now on justice is given to my people. Chang-i shall be set free. Ahmad's body shall be thrown to the dogs in the street and all his wealth shall be distributed among the poor." Then the Great Khan smiled upon Marco, and turned to his courtiers. "This is a man of great courage," he told them. "He fights on the side of the just."

CHAPTER TEN

A New Post for Marco

THREE busy years flew by for Marco. One
spring morning, he stood again in front of the
Great Khan. The Emperor was speaking
gravely.

"Messer Marco Polo," he said, "I am
pleased with the work you are doing at this
great court. You are respected by men and
women and children, and all in Kanbalu affec-
tionately call you the Noble Venetian."

Marco Polo bowed as the Great Khan
paused.

"Your words of praise, O Illustrious Emperor," he said, "please me very much."

The Great Khan nodded graciously.

"You are a man of sense as well as a speaker
of many languages. It is fitting now that I

should appoint you to another important post in my service."

Again the Great Khan paused, and Marco acknowledged his speech.

"I shall do my best to serve you, O Lord of Lords, in any way you see fit."

The Great Khan rose from his golden chair.

"Messer Marco Polo," he said, "I am told that you are a fearless traveler, and that you are not afraid of either man or beast. Nor do you, they say, lose your head in a crisis.

"I proclaim you now my Imperial Commissioner. You will travel in distant parts of my kingdom. You will be expected to study conditions in these countries. You must return to me with a full report of what you have seen in far provinces and what you have heard the people, as well as their rulers, say."

Marco Polo smiled and bowed to the floor. "I will strive to serve you well, O Illustrious Emperor," he said. "The duties you have given me fill me with delight."

The Great Khan made a royal gesture with his painted fan.

"The first province which you must visit, Messer Marco Polo," he said, "is the province of Yünnan. You will travel through very dangerous country. It may take you four moons to reach Yünnan." The Emperor ended with a blessing: "May Fate be kind to you, Messer Marco Polo, and all celestial beings guard you."

Again Marco Polo voiced his thanks. The Great Khan folded his hands in the brocaded sleeves of his ceremonial gown. The audience was over.

So Marco was to be Imperial Commissioner and go to the province of Yünnan! He hastened to tell his father and his uncle Maffeo. They were overjoyed at this honor that had come to him.

"You will travel in a caravan fit for a prince!" his father said happily.

"Before you start on your journey," his uncle Maffeo advised him, "you must have the astrologers chart your way by the stars."

Before many weeks went by, all preparations for the journey to Yünnan were made. The caravan made up for Marco was as princely as his father had said it would be. There were scores of fine horses, stores of good food, and tents so luxurious that they looked like royal pavilions.

A camel train was included in the caravan, for use in places where it would be hard for horses to travel. There were also many servants and an armed guard.

"Who is to be the caravan master?" Chen Fu asked Marco excitedly.

"One of the best in the Great Khan's service," answered Marco. "His name is Wu Ling."

Much to Chen Fu's delight, Marco Polo had decided to take him along to Yünnan, to take care of Shiraz and to help in other ways.

Chen Fu had been in Marco's service several years now. He had grown tall and strong and knew how to serve his master well.

Soon the day came on which the astrologers had advised Marco to start upon his journey.

Marco bid his father an affectionate goodby. "Have no fears for me," he said. "Has not Wu Ling been teaching me how to protect myself? I even know how to handle a rope!"

The caravan passed through the Gate of the Lanterns, leaving the capital city behind. Ten miles out from Kanbalu, it crossed a magnificent bridge. Then it wended its way through many strange cities. Everywhere the caravan stopped, Marco Polo was received with all the pomp and ceremony which was due an Imperial Commissioner.

At first, he was honored because of his position, but when the people came to know him, Marco was honored because of himself. He was gay and loved laughter. He had none of

the solemnity that Imperial Commissioners usually had. This pleased the people and they liked the Noble Venetian.

The caravan crossed the wide Yellow River which was filled with ocean-going ships. Marco Polo went aboard the ships and inspected them for the Great Khan. They made him think of his boyhood days when he and Christopher had enjoyed the Arsenal so much.

The Chinese ships surprised him. They were much bigger and far more comfortable than any galley he had ever seen in Venice.

"When I was a boy," he told Chen Fu, "I loved ships as much as you love horses!"

After weeks of travel, they came to the Pe Lu, which was the name for an ancient caravan road. For many, many years, caravans had traveled on it to carry silk from old Cathay across the desert to Antioch. The Great Khan's grandfather, Chinghis Khan, had named it the Silk Road.

Marco was riding at the head of the caravan as they approached it. They would only cross this road, then wend their way south.

"Look how busy the Silk Road is!" Marco cried to Chen Fu. "The camel caravans seem endless! I am told that they are carrying silks and spices and ivory and furs."

Chen Fu looked at the busy scene. "I think everyone in the world must be here, Honorable Commissioner!" he exclaimed. "See those priests wearing high yellow hats and walking along swinging prayer wheels!"

[*111*]

"I believe they come from Tibet," Marco Polo observed.

But Chen Fu hardly heard him. He was watching a sad sight.

"Here come a lot of slave girls, tied together like strings of horses!" he said. "I am glad we did not let Mulan be sold as a slave."

"So am I," agreed Marco Polo. "They are doubtless taking those poor girls to slave markets on the coast."

"And look at the beggars!" added Chen Fu. "They are here by the hundreds!"

"I'm afraid you can find beggars nearly everywhere in Cathay," Marco said.

There was a break in the long stream of travelers and he led the caravan across the road. The caravan moved on toward the south. Presently it reached the mysterious country of Tibet. Here were mountains higher than any in the world. The caravan master led the way now, through foothills that were thick with ancient bamboo forests.

One morning he said, "From now on, we face great danger, men. We shall have to be on our guard against fierce lions and tigers. And if we should be caught in a storm, beware of men of magic!"

"What have they to do with storms?" Marco Polo asked.

"They have the power to create great thunderstorms," replied the caravan master soberly. "They do this to trap travelers into seeking refuge in their castles. Once they have them under their roofs, they are said to do terrible things to them."

The forest was dark and threatening. Again and again there came the far-off cry of eagles above the mountain peaks. As the caravan went on, several mountain lions were killed

[113]

by the armed guards. Marco watched one wounded lion fall down from a tree to die upon the ground.

"It is a noble-looking beast," he said. "Its eyes are as beautiful as topaz."

When they had passed through the forest, the caravan came to desolate country. Here and there a lonely castle looked down from a rocky crag. Again Wu Ling, the caravan master, warned the travelers. "The men of magic live in those castles," he said. "They are wicked Enchanters whom I hope we will not see."

"But what do they look like?" asked Marco.

The caravan master frowned.

"They have long black beards and wear high black, pointed hats. They all carry whips and ride black horses."

Marco Polo was calm, but Chen Fu shuddered. "They certainly sound like a gruesome lot," said Marco.

The following day, he and Chen Fu rode a little behind the caravan. Marco had stopped his horse to watch a strange little animal cavorting on the ground. It was giving off an odor which he had been told was the musk from which fine perfumes were made. Chen Fu was also watching it with interest.

Suddenly Shiraz pawed the ground, seemingly without a reason. Her lovely eyes were large with fear.

"Steady, Shiraz!" Marco patted her head. "What are you afraid of? This little beast won't hurt you!"

Again she pawed nervously. Chen Fu looked around and gave a startled cry. As if he had come right out of the ground, a rider on a great black horse appeared suddenly at Chen Fu's side. He wore a high, pointed hat and carried a long whip.

"It's an Enchanter!" cried Marco Polo. "Ride on, Chen Fu! We'll overtake the caravan! Ride on!"

He spoke a word to Shiraz, who galloped away as if she had wings.

Chen Fu dug his spurs into his horse, but he was already too late. The Enchanter had grasped his bridle.

"Ride with me," he commanded Chen Fu, "or I will kill you!"

Chen Fu sat upon his saddle, paralyzed with fear. The Enchanter raised himself from his horse. As if he were in the clutches of a big black bat, Chen Fu felt himself lifted from his horse and placed upon the Enchanter's.

[*115*]

"Help!" he cried out wildly before the Enchanter could cover his mouth. "Help!"

Marco Polo heard his cry. He turned Shiraz around in a flash and rode hotly after the Enchanter. Meanwhile, he called to an armed guard riding some distance ahead, "Go on! I will meet you at the Burma Road!"

He gained upon the Enchanter before they had gone a mile. He could see a road leading to a castle perched high upon a cliff. Marco decided that the Enchanter was planning to take Chen Fu to this castle.

"Nothing must happen to Chen Fu!" he vowed. "Why, he is like a younger brother!"

Marco gave the reins to Shiraz, who galloped on and on. Suddenly he blinked, fearing he was stricken with blindness. All was darkness around him. A moment later he realized what had happened. "It's the work of the Enchanter!" he muttered. "He's creating a storm!"

Sharp arrows of rain began to fall. Thunder rolled from the cliff above the castle. Bright streaks of lightning dazzled him, but he kept riding on.

Again he gained on the Enchanter. Whenever the lightning made the landscape bright,

"Help!" Chen Fu cried out wildly

he could see the black-robed man riding on.

Presently Marco realized that he was riding beside a deep gully. The lightning flashed, and far ahead he saw a bridge built over the gully. He realized that the Enchanter would have to cross this bridge if he wished to reach the castle.

Quickly Marco urged Shiraz down into the gully and up the other side. When the Enchanter reached the bridge, Marco was already on the far end, seated firmly on Shiraz, and facing him.

The Enchanter brought his horse to a dead stop. Marco raised himself high on his saddle. He uncoiled one of the ropes which he carried on his saddle. Skillfully he threw it. It dropped down over Chen Fu's head and around his waist.

Chen Fu could feel Marco Polo pulling him off the Enchanter's horse. The Enchanter struggled hard to prevent it. Chen Fu felt like a bundle of rags being pulled this way and that in a tug-of-war.

Thunder roared above the castle and lightning streaked across the bridge. Finally Chen Fu was pulled to Marco's side. He climbed up on Shiraz and sat behind Marco.

"Quiet!" ordered Marco, as Chen Fu was about to speak.

Marco uncoiled and threw another rope. As it dropped down over the Enchanter's head and settled around his neck, Marco pulled on it hard. With a strangled cry, the magician toppled off his horse. Again Marco pulled on the rope without mercy.

"Die, you wicked magician! Die!" Marco cried.

Again the lightning made the landscape bright. Chen Fu saw the black-robed man lying in a heap upon the bridge.

Marco Polo had killed the Enchanter to save Chen Fu's life.

CHAPTER ELEVEN

The Battle of the Elephants

"WHY did the Imperial Commissioner leave the caravan?" Wu Ling asked the guard.

"I have no way of knowing," the guard answered. "I only heard him shout that he would meet us at the Burma Road."

The caravan master thought for a moment before he made a decision.

"We will not go on to the Burma Road without him," he told his men. "We'll camp here and wait. If Marco Polo does not join us by sundown, we'll send out scouts to find him. This is dangerous country."

Much to the joy of everyone in the caravan, Marco and Chen Fu reached the camp by midafternoon. Marco brought Shiraz to a stop in front of Wu Ling's tent.

"The gods be praised!" cried the caravan master. "And may I ask, O Honorable Commissioner, why you departed from us in haste?"

To the wide-eyed amazement of everyone in the caravan, Marco told the story of the wicked Enchanter. How he had tried to kidnap Chen Fu—how he had created a storm—and how the rescue had been made.

The caravan master smiled. "You are a lucky boy, Chen Fu," he said. "The Honorable Commissioner has done a very brave thing."

Marco Polo spoke modestly.

"It is to you, Wu Ling, that we owe our thanks. If you had not taught me how to handle a rope before we left Kanbalu—"

The caravan master smiled again.

"All who travel by caravan should know how to handle a rope with skill," he declared. "The Tartars depend on ropes to take captives as much as they depend on knives and swords! I was trained how to protect myself when I was a boy. And now," he went on pleasantly, "come into my tent and we'll chart the next lap of our journey."

Marco told Chen Fu to take Shiraz out to pasture. Then he followed Wu Ling into his tent.

[*121*]

"I hope we can reach the Burma Road tomorrow," Marco said eagerly.

Wu Ling sat down at a table littered with notes and charts.

"We will reach it tomorrow and follow it for ten days," he said. "By that time we should arrive at Tali, a town on the shore of a big lake."

Marco made a note on a chart that lay before him.

"When we get to Yünnan," he said, "I am charged by the Great Khan to get a full report on the Battle of the Elephants. It was an historic battle because it was the first time that elephants were ever used against him in warfare."

Wu Ling smiled his friendly smile. "That was a great battle, sir," he said.

"The Great Khan wants to know all about it in detail," Marco went on, "so that he, too, may make use of elephants in future wars of his own."

"That is a good reason," the caravan master said. Then he stood up and bowed to Marco. "And now, Honorable Commissioner, it would be wise for you to get some rest. The caravan will leave at sunrise."

By evening of the following day, the caravan had reached the Burma Road. Marco was eager to see this storied highway that wound its way through towering mountains.

"It is as narrow as a mule track!" he exclaimed when he first saw it.

From dizzy heights to level plains in deep green valleys, the road ran through dark and dangerous places. Some said that it was a haunted road. Haunted or not, it was the ancient caravan route for all who made the journey from Old Cathay to Burma.

[*123*]

As the caravan traveled along the road, Marco Polo observed many things.

"Who are those magnificent horsemen?" he asked Wu Ling as a galloping band of riders dashed by.

Wu Ling looked at them with distrust.

"Pay no attention to them," he warned, "or we will be asking for trouble! They carry poisoned arrows and it takes but one to kill you!"

When they came to the town of Tali, Marco stood on the shore of the lake and looked down into the water. Chen Fu was standing beside him.

"Look, Honorable Commissioner! Look!" Chen Fu cried excitedly. "What are those big things flopping about?"

"Those big things, Chen Fu," said Wu Ling, coming up behind them, "are crocodiles!"

"Crocodiles!" echoed Marco Polo. "They look ferocious!"

They watched one of the creatures raise its ugly head to drink.

"They are most ferocious, Honorable Commissioner," explained Wu Ling. "Many of them are bigger than you are and have terrible jaws which open wide enough to swallow a man!"

Chen Fu took a frightened step backward. "I wouldn't want to swim in this lake!" he cried.

Suddenly one of the crocodiles stared at them with glaring eyes.

"Let us hasten away from here," Wu Ling said nervously. "This beast looks ready to go hunting!"

"Do they actually hunt?" asked Marco in surprise, as Wu Ling led the way from the lake up a steep embankment.

"Yes, they really hunt," Wu Ling answered grimly. "Sometimes they even go to tigers' lairs to capture young cubs. If the mother tiger puts up a fight, it is a battle to the death, and the crocodile always wins."

Chen Fu started running. "I want no part of crocodiles!" he called back comically over his shoulder.

After several more days of travel, the caravan crossed the great Yangtze River. Now they were in Yünnan. This was the province which the Great Khan had sent Marco Polo to inspect. Here Marco would aim to accomplish his mission.

"Listen to the golden trumpets!" cried Chen Fu. "They are blowing for you, Honorable Commissioner!"

They were approaching the castle of the ruler of the province. Marco Polo was sitting

proudly on Shiraz, wearing a rich cloak embroidered with jewels. He was now a fine-looking young man, twenty-five years old.

People lined the streets of the capital city to greet him.

"Long live the Imperial Commissioner!" they cheered. "He is sent to us by the Great Khan!"

The Governor of Yünnan had sent many fine horses and riders to conduct Marco Polo to his palace. Gongmen walked before them sounding glittering gongs. Drummers, dressed in crimson and gold, beat big drums with painted drumsticks.

Marco Polo was led into the audience hall of the castle. He stood before the ruler and bowed low.

"Greetings, Sire, from Kublai Khan, Illustrious Emperor, Lord of Lords, and All-Powerful Ruler of Cathay," he said.

The Governor rose from his jeweled chair.

"Greetings, Imperial Commissioner! It is the pleasure of all Yünnan to greet you!"

Later in the day, Marco Polo was conducted into one of the inner rooms of the palace. It was a beautiful room, hung with richly colored tapestries woven by the royal weavers. Each tapestry told a story. On each was a scene which showed a part of the historic Battle of the Elephants.

"Most Wise Commissioner," said the Governor of Yünnan, "look at these pictures and

see just how the battle was fought. I have had
my weavers put it into pictures to preserve its
story for us."

Marco Polo was deeply impressed. "This is a wonderful thing," he said. Then he studied the tapestry showing the beginning of the battle. "I see that the fighting began on a plain in the Taiping Valley," he said.

The Governor nodded.

"The Great Khan's army had only twelve thousand archers," he told Marco. "But the troops from Burma who fought against us had two thousand elephants and sixty thousand men!"

"Then we were cruelly outnumbered from the beginning," said Marco.

The Governor traced the outline of a picture rich in coloring.

"You can see that each elephant carried something on his back which was like a little castle. Spearmen and archers rode in it. They

[*129*]

attacked our soldiers who were on foot, and those in the cavalry."

"The elephants must have had the advantage," Marco Polo said, "because they could trample our men down."

The Governor nodded and pointed to the next tapestry.

"Look at this and you can see what a bloody battle it was. We could not have won if we had not had a very wise general. He realized that the troops from Burma had not put enough armor on their elephants. So he urged our men to shoot volleys and volleys of arrows. The elephants were so badly wounded that they were soon out of control."

After a pause he added, respectfully, "In the name of the Great Khan, the general led us to a victory greater than we had ever known."

Marco Polo studied the tapestries with deep interest. He realized that if elephants were properly covered with armor, it would be a great advantage to use them in warfare.

He praised the general's clever use of the ground on which the battle had been fought. The troops of Yünnan had been so placed that they had a forest behind them and could take refuge in it, if necessary. This was intelligent

[130]

planning, because the enemy had no such woods to which to retreat.

Marco turned to the Governor, who still stood at his side.

"There are certain things in these pictures," he said, "by which I can trace the way in which this battle was fought. I shall study them until I have learned every detail, so I may report the general's tactics to the Great Khan."

Several months later, when he had returned to Kanbalu, Marco Polo made his report on the Battle of the Elephants. He summed up the reasons why the great army from Burma had been defeated in spite of its use of elephants. So clear and intelligent was his reporting that the Great Khan praised him.

"I like the way you tell things, Marco Polo," he said. "You do not give me dry-as-dust reports. You are serious when you must be, but you are also gay. My other commissioners bore me."

Marco Polo bowed to the floor and said: "Your service is my delight, O Illustrious Emperor."

The Great Khan smiled a gracious smile. "You have shown me, Messer Marco Polo, that you have an understanding of warfare that is astonishing. I think you have the makings of a commander of men." The Khan stood up and waved his ivory fan. "In recognition of the value of your services, I appoint you now to the post of Royal Governor of the city of Yangchow."

CHAPTER TWELVE

Marco, the Map Maker

WHAT will the city of Yangchow be like?"
Mulan asked Marco Polo, when she heard that
he was to govern it.

Marco smiled. "It is a beautiful city,
Mulan," he answered. "The richest in all
Cathay! There are many pagodas and palaces.
I am told that nightingales nest in flowering
trees and there will be ginger blossoms in my
garden!"

Mulan's big dark eyes lighted with pleasure.
"I like ginger blossoms," she said. "Some day
I'll wear them in my hair."

Marco smiled again. "I'll bring you a bou-
quet," he promised, "when I come back. And
I'll tell you all about the city."

A day or two later, he left Kanbalu. When
he reached Yangchow, Marco found the whole
populace eagerly awaiting him. They were

glad they were to have such a young and gracious governor. Marco Polo ruled them wisely for three busy years. He found them to be skilled workers and artists.

He had taken Chen Fu to Yangchow with him.

"You are growing tall, Chen Fu," he said to the boy one day. "Soon you will be seventeen! I think I shall make you one of my aides because you have been so faithful."

"One of your aides!" Chen Fu was wide-eyed. Then he suddenly remembered what he had called Marco Polo when he was a little boy, and exclaimed, "Oh, Walking Giant!"

Marco Polo laughed aloud.

"I always liked that name, Chen Fu," he said. "And when I take to traveling again, I will have to have the legs of a giant to take me everywhere that I shall have to go!"

Chen Fu was happy. He liked to travel with Marco Polo. He hoped they would soon be off to far places again!

When they returned to Kanbalu, the Great Khan sent for Marco.

"You have served me wisely as the Governor of Yangchow, but now I have a new use for you," he said. Suddenly he smiled. "I think you have too many talents to be kept in one place."

Marco bowed before the Great Khan, saying: "When you speak to me of traveling, O Lord of Lords, I seem to feel the wind pushing at my back."

Again the Great Khan smiled.

"There are countries beyond our borders that I want you to explore. I want you to bring me reports on how the people live, how they

[*135*]

are governed, and what gods they believe in. I also want to know what natural resources exist in each country and how well the people are armed."

Marco Polo bowed to the floor this time. "I will keep my eyes open and make many notes," he answered.

The Great Khan leaned forward in his jeweled chair. "You will be First Lord of Geography as well as my ambassador. You will be going to places where no European has ever been. Perhaps no man of our own race has been to those places either. I am told that you draw maps well."

Marco Polo spoke modestly. "I have made maps of places I have visited so that other men who wish to travel to them may find their way. Maps are scarce on this great continent."

"I hope, then," said the Khan, "that you will draw other maps as you go along. And there is one thing more. Your father tells me that you know something of the laws of navigation."

Marco Polo smiled. "I have loved ships and the sea, O Great Khan, since I was a boy. I learned to navigate ships when we made our first voyage across the China Sea."

The Great Khan glanced at his notes which had been made on rice paper.

"You will command a fleet which is to go to Siam and Sumatra and the Andaman Islands," he said. "From there you'll embark for Ceylon where you will engage in a secret mission."

"A secret mission?" Marco repeated curiously.

The Great Khan spoke in a low voice.

"There are certain relics there that I want you to buy for me. They are sacred to the great god Buddha. There is also a ruby said to be the finest in the world. No one must know you wish to buy them until you set foot in Ceylon. It will take much skill to acquire them, because they are not for sale."

"I understand," Marco Polo replied gravely. "And I will try to bargain well."

The Great Khan picked up a scroll from a table beside his golden chair.

"This is a sealed order," he said. "It will instruct you how much to offer the King of Ceylon for these treasures. Keep it in your possession and do not consult it until you are ready to talk to the king."

Marco took the scroll and put it in the leather pouch he always wore at his waist.

[*137*]

"I will guard it with my life," he promised.

The Great Khan rose to give Marco his blessing. "May the Gods of Springtime Light go with you."

Sumatra and Siam! The faraway Andaman Islands! The fabulous Isle of Jewels, radiant Ceylon! As the voice of the Great Khan had

called off the names of these places, Marco Polo had fancied that he heard the sound of golden bells calling him to come. But he realized, too, that there would be dangers on his journey.

The day soon came when the great voyage began. Marco Polo set sail from Cathay with two thousand men. He was given a fleet of Chinese ships, each with a crew of three hundred. The ships had splendid sails and were even more seaworthy than any he had seen as a boy in Venice.

The fleet sailed south on the China Sea. It put into ports where Marco saw many new things. He recorded the descriptions of foreign streets and strange people in his notebook. He made drawings of places he had never seen before and charted the roads to them accurately.

One afternoon he stood on the deck of the flagship with Chen Fu at his side.

"We are in the Malay Peninsula now," Marco Polo told Chen Fu. "Soon we will be in the Malay Straits, then a thousand-mile crossing will bring us to Sumatra."

"Shall we stay in Sumatra a long time?" asked Chen Fu.

"Not so long," answered Marco. "We must go on to the place where I must carry out a secret mission."

When he had planned to stay "not so long" in Sumatra, Marco Polo had reckoned without the weather.

A southwesterly monsoon was blowing in

the Bay of Bengal. Not even the sails of these Chinese ships could stand the storm and fury of it. Howling winds tossed the fleet this way and that until the ships seemed lost among the monstrous waves like bits of helpless timber.

"Put into Sumatra and stay there!" Marco Polo commanded the crews.

It was on Sumatra that he first saw an animal called the unicorn. It looked like a white horse, but it had one straight horn growing out from its forehead.

"Truly a strange animal!" he exclaimed to Chen Fu.

"And look at this, Walking Giant!" Chen Fu put his hand against a huge tree. "The natives call it a flour tree. All you have to do is cut it down and split it open. Its trunk is full of a pithy substance like flour, which can be made into bread!"

Marco Polo smiled at Chen Fu's enthusiasm. "Truly a wondrous tree!" he said. "I will make a note of it for the Great Khan!"

The monsoon continued for five long months. Marco Polo's expedition was forced to camp on the island.

Unicorns and flour trees were not the only new things they saw on Sumatra. Far up in the mountains lived a race of men so wicked that they ate human flesh. Natives called them cannibals. It was said that they ate only two kinds of people—close relatives and foreigners.

"We must be on our guard against them," Marco told his men. "We'll build castles of logs and dig ditches around them. These ditches will lead to the open sea so we can take to our ships in case these beastlike men attack!"

Chen Fu looked very sober.

"I would rather die in the monsoon," he said, "than be eaten by a cannibal!"

Even Marco Polo looked a bit sober. Would the cannibals try to capture them in this wild and dangerous country?

But the fury of the monsoon kept the wicked cannibals in their mountain strongholds. When the monsoon was over, Marco Polo's fleet sailed away in haste.

It was not until they left the Andaman Islands that Marco Polo told his men that they were going on to the island of Ceylon. There he would try to carry out his secret mission.

The newly painted sails of the fleet billowed in the wind. The prows of all the ships were turned toward the Indian Ocean.

Howling winds tossed the fleet this way and that

"Listen!" cried Marco when at last the travelers set foot on the island of Ceylon. "What wondrous music is that?"

"The temple bells are ringing," answered an aide who walked at his side. "The temple bells of Ceylon are far-famed for their music."

Marco Polo smiled. "It is right that temple bells should ring," he thought, "because I have come here to buy sacred relics for the Khan."

Suddenly he stopped beside a tree that looked somewhat like a palm tree. It seemed a curious thing to see native boys breaking off its branches. Some of them were holding the branches to their lips and sucking hard upon them. Others were putting branches into open vessels.

"What kind of tree is this?" he asked the native boys.

One of them smiled a big smile. "This is a gomuti palm, sir," he answered. "The juice from its branches makes wine. The trees are really known as wine trees." The boy held up a branch to Marco's lips. "Taste, sir!" he said.

Marco tasted an excellent beverage.

"These are wonderful, wonderful trees," he said, "these wine trees of Ceylon!"

Royal courtiers came to meet him and conducted him to the king's palace.

Many pilgrims came to Ceylon who, like Marco Polo, were in quest of the sacred relics of Buddha, the great god of the East. It was said that the relics were kept in a temple called the Temple of the Tooth. This shrine stood on a holy mountain known as Adam's Peak.

"It will not be easy to get any of these relics," Marco Polo told the men who accompanied him. "The King of Ceylon may refuse to sell them at any price."

Before he was presented to the monarch, Marco broke the seal upon the scroll which the Great Khan had given him. He was amazed when he found out how much the Khan would allow him to pay for the treasures.

He was presented to the monarch, who received him graciously, and he begged the king to permit him to buy the relics which the Great Khan wanted. After a long argument, the king let him have two molar teeth and a lock of Buddha's hair.

The teeth and hair of the mystic Buddha! How pleased the Khan would be to learn that this part of Marco's task had been well done.

"And now," said Marco Polo, "I should like

to bargain for the great god's begging bowl."

At first the king refused even to talk about this precious relic. But Marco Polo offered to pay so much for it that the king agreed at last to sell the exquisite green bowl used by Buddha. It was given to Marco Polo to take back to the Great Khan.

Then Marco prostrated himself before the King of Ceylon. "Most Honored Monarch," he said very reverently, "I am charged by the Great Khan with yet another mission."

"What is its nature?" asked the king.

"The island of Ceylon," Marco said earnestly, "is the Isle of Precious Jewels. It produces more valuable sapphires, topazes, amethysts, and other valuable stones than are found in any other part of the world. I am told that you possess a certain ruby that is the grandest ever seen. It is said to look like a glowing fire and to be the largest ruby in the world!"

The king was silent for a moment. Then he rose from his glittering throne.

"Honorable Marco Polo," he said, "do not ask me to bargain for this ruby. I would not sell it for all the treasures in the universe!"

"But Most Gracious Monarch," protested

Marco Polo gasped aloud at its flaming beauty

Marco Polo, "I am charged by the Great Khan to offer you the value of a city to obtain it!"

The king made a royal gesture. "Bring the treasured ruby before us!" he ordered his royal guards.

The ruby was brought on a white silken pillow. Marco Polo gasped aloud at its flaming beauty. "I can offer you the value of a city!" he reminded the king.

Then the king did a curious thing. He took the ruby from the pillow and touched it to his face.

"This precious stone belonged to my ancestors," he said solemnly. "It has a magical quality that preserves one's youth and health. I could not sell it without great dishonor, not even if there were a thousand khans in Cathay and each one offered me the value of a city!"

Again Marco looked at the ruby, so full of fire and magic. He was disappointed that he had been unable to get it for the Great Khan. Suddenly he realized that he was not alone in his failure. No one else in the world could ever buy this precious stone!

The King of Ceylon rose from his throne. Marco Polo bowed. The audience was over.

CHAPTER THIRTEEN

Precious Cargo

THE fleet sailed on to many other countries. Before it returned to Cathay, Marco Polo had explored the greater part of the whole known world.

He had done what the Great Khan expected of him. His notebooks were filled with accounts of strange people and places. He had made fascinating drawings of each country he had visited. And he had charted his route with such care that explorers were able to follow in his footsteps for centuries to come.

He had heard myths and legends from tellers of tales in many lands. He had studied the odd customs of the people and listened to their native music. He had looked upon jewels that made up the wealth of ancient kingdoms. Fantastic birds and trees, fierce animals roaming in distant jungles, all had been observed by him with curiosity and remembered in detail.

He had also made notes of foreign armies and weapons. From Marco Polo's reports, the Great Khan learned what he might expect if the kings of these various countries became his future enemies.

"Well done, Marco Polo," the Great Khan said, most pleased. "Of all the courtiers in my service you are the most valuable."

Marco Polo was glad to be back from his wanderings. He enjoyed his reunion with his father and his uncle Maffeo. One afternoon as they sat in a gilded pavilion, Messer Nicolo said, "We have news for you, my son."

Marco smiled at him with affection.

"Good news?" he asked.

His father smiled too.

"Your uncle Maffeo and I want to leave Cathay and go back home to Venice."

Marco stood up in surprise.

"Go back to Venice!" he echoed.

"Wouldn't you like to go back, too?" his uncle Maffeo asked.

Suddenly Marco realized that he would love to go back home. He was weary of pomp and ceremony. Tired of all the curious things in

[149]

the East. It would seem very good to see the family mansion facing the canal. Was Rosa still there, he wondered? And Signor Gilberto?

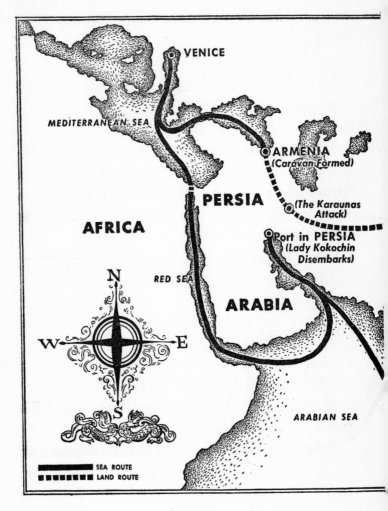

"I can think of nothing better," he told his father and uncle, "than to go back home again."

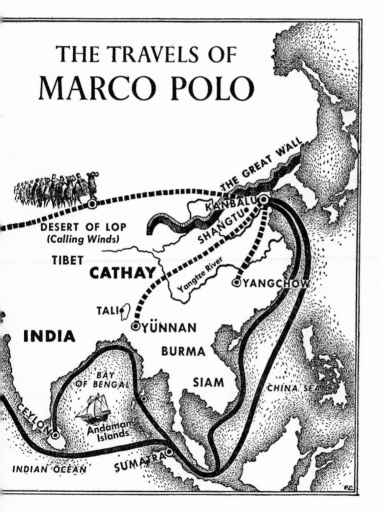

"We will have to ask the Great Khan's permission," his father reminded him.

"Let us try to do so at once!" Marco exclaimed and his face brightened at the thought of seeing places he had loved in his boyhood.

Seventeen years had passed since the Polos had arrived in Cathay. During all that time, the Great Khan had seldom refused to grant them whatever they asked.

The Khan had made Marco his favorite courtier. He had also permitted the elder Polos to conduct their trade as merchants in his kingdom. This had made them rich beyond their dreams. Yes, gifts and honors he had heaped upon all three. But when Messer Nicolo prostrated himself before him and asked leave to go home, the Great Khan was amazed.

"Why do you wish to go home?" he cried. "Suppose that you should die on the way?" His dark eyes looked bewildered. "If you have need of more gold, just tell me! I will give you more of it than you could ever find at home!"

"O Great and Noble Khan," Messer Nicolo protested, "it is not gold we seek! We only want to see our native land."

The Khan shook his head.

"No, Messer Nicolo Polo, I will not let you go. Nothing can persuade me to allow you to depart from my realm."

Time and time again, the Polos appeared before the Khan, but his answer was always the same. Five more restless years went by. Then one day the Great Khan sent for them.

"The time has come when I must permit you to leave Cathay," he said. "There is a mission that only you, Marco Polo, can be trusted to accomplish."

"Name it, Great Khan," said Marco.

The Emperor sighed.

"Our little Princess Kokochin is to be married to the King of Persia," he said, "and she must be taken to his palace. She cannot travel overland, since a war is being fought in one of the countries along the way. Therefore she must travel by sea."

He paused for a moment. Then he added, "I should like to keep you Polos here with me. But I value the happiness of the little princess far above my own. If you will promise to sail with her to Persia and to deliver her safely to the king, I will grant your wish and allow you to return to Venice."

Marco bowed before the throne.

[153]

"I swear that I will deliver the Lady Koko-chin to Persia," he said. "I swear this on my honor."

"So be it, then," said the Great Khan.

The elder Polos also bowed.

"O Wise and Mighty Khan," they said, "accept our deepest gratitude. We will depart from Cathay with love and devotion for you in our hearts. Your kindness to us outshines the gold of the sun and the silver of the moon."

The Great Khan smiled graciously.

"I bear a deep affection for you all," he told them. "Go now, with my blessing."

So it came about that after many years, the Polos made preparations to return to Venice. Fourteen ships were placed at their disposal. Some of them were rigged to carry twelve splendid sails.

Chen Fu and Mulan were sad when the time came for Marco Polo to leave Cathay. They followed him to the port of Zayton from which the ships were to sail.

"Farewell, O Honorable Marco Polo," Mulan said and her almond eyes were filled with tears.

Marco put one arm around her and the other around Chen Fu.

"I will remember and love you both all the days of my life," he told them

"I will remember and love you both all the days of my life," he told them.

Although he was a young man now, Chen Fu's voice was choked with grief.

"Farewell, Honorable Marco Polo!" he cried. "Oh, dear Walking Giant! Farewell!"

Many courtiers assembled on the deck of the flagship. They gave the Polos parting presents of diamonds and rubies and other beautiful jewels, in the name of the Great Khan.

Presently the farewells were over. The Lady Kokochin was brought aboard followed by her favorite pet, a gorgeous bird of paradise. Sails were unfurled. The courtiers left the flagship and all was made ready for the departure.

Marco Polo looked his last at pagodas in the sun. Again he waved to Mulan and Chen Fu. Then fourteen glorious ships moved majestically to sea.

CHAPTER FOURTEEN

Beggars at the Door

MARCO POLO accomplished his mission. He delivered the lovely Lady Kokochin to the King of Persia. The Polos then said farewell to the fleet and began their long journey home. After much weary traveling by land as well as sea, they arrived in Venice.

Venice! They saw it first from the deck as the ship sailed into the Arsenal. Marco's heart almost sang as he saw the spice ships with saffron-colored sails in the harbor, just as they had been when he was a little boy.

Now he was a man, over forty years old. He not only recognized the ships from the Far East, but he had been in the places from which they had sailed and knew what kind of people lived in those countries.

"Marco," said his father, "look at the Palace

of the Doges! It gleams in the sunlight like mother-of-pearl."

Marco answered him merrily: "And the Grand Canal is cluttered with traffic just as it always was! I feared we would never see it again, during our dangerous journey."

Messer Maffeo spoke soberly.

There is one thing," he said, "of which I am not proud. We have lived in Cathay so long that we scarcely know how to speak our own language."

"It will soon come back to us when we speak to others," Marco comforted him. "Wait until we talk to Rosa and Signor Gilberto!" Suddenly he laughed. "And if Christopher is in Venice, he will soon teach us what we have forgotten!"

The Polos did not look like wealthy travelers, and they certainly did not look like natives of Venice. They were wearing strange garments of the sort they had worn in Cathay. Their clothes were not only strange. They were shabby.

Marco and his father and his uncle Maffeo looked like three bronzed strangers out of the East, too poor to be honored, and too threadbare to be given even a second glance.

When they came off the ship, they went at once to their old home. There were tears in their eyes at the sight of the fine old family mansion.

"There were times in Cathay when I almost believed that we should never see our home again," said Marco.

He opened the wrought-iron entrance gate. They walked into the inner courtyard and up the steps of the piazza.

"There is no one here," said Marco's father.

"There must be someone somewhere," Marco spoke cheerfully. "I will ring the visitor's bell."

He rang the big bell loudly. Soon a plump woman he dimly recognized as Rosa came through the garden at the side of the house. A small boy raced ahead of her.

"Look, Grandmother, look!" he cried. "There are beggars at the door!"

Rosa thrust her hands under her apron and waved it threateningly at the Polos.

"Begone, you vagrants! Begone!" she cried.

Marco took long steps to her side. Before she could cry out again, he took both her hands in his.

"Rosa! Rosa!" he said, laughing. "Don't

[*159*]

you know your own bambino? It is Marco, Rosa, Marco!"

"*Bambino!*" she exclaimed, wide-eyed. "But no! You are not Marco. No!"

"But I am, Rosa!" Marco insisted. "I have come home to stay! And here are my father and uncle!"

Rosa looked at him steadily.

"Marco," she repeated. "Are you really Marco?" Suddenly she threw her arms wide open and smiled. "You are my bambino! Oh, Marco mio!"

Rosa was not the only one who did not recognize the Polos. Even their own relatives insisted that these strange-looking men could not
be the Noble Venetians who had gone away so
many years before.

"You had better put them out of the house!"
they said angrily to Rosa. "How can you be so
sure that they are the Polos?"

Rosa stood up for the so-called strangers.

"They say that they can prove who they
are!" she told the relatives. "You can at least
give them the chance!"

"But how can they prove it?" the relatives
persisted.

"The Polos," said Rosa, "want you all to
come to a banquet. They say they will prove
to you then that they are whom they claim
to be."

The relatives were not eager to accept the
invitation. They decided, however, to attend
the banquet. Marco wished that Christopher
might be there, for he felt sure that his cousin
would recognize him. But Christopher was not
in Venice. Marco would have to wait until he
came in from his father's farm of which he was
now master.

On the night of the banquet the Polos appeared before their guests in magnificent robes of crimson damask. They sat at the head of a long oak table loaded with fine food, fresh fruits, and wine.

When the feasting was over, Marco went into the next room. A moment later he returned, carrying the travel-stained garments the Polos had worn when they had arrived in Venice.

"Clear a space on the table!" he ordered.

The servants removed the golden plates. Marco tossed the travel-worn garments in a heap on the table. The guests looked on, bewildered.

"I want to prove to you," said Marco, "that we are not strangers, but the Polos whom we claim to be!"

He took a sharp knife and opened the seams of the old clothes. He ripped out the linings, then he shook the clothes lightly.

The guests gasped with surprise. To their utter amazement, a shower of jewels fell down upon the table. Every guest at the table stood up. Great quantities of sapphires, diamonds, rubies, emeralds, and other beautiful gems had been hidden in the tattered garments. By hiding the jewels in this way, the Polos had

A shower of jewels fell down upon the table

been able to bring them safely to Venice.

At the sight of so much wealth before their very eyes, one guest spoke for all the others.

"These men are not strangers," he said. "They are truly the Polos, who have traveled far and returned at last from the rich lands of the East."

At that moment the door to the banquet room was flung open. A handsome middle-aged man looked over the people in the room. Then he strode directly up to Marco. He had not even seen the clothes and the jewels. Nor had he heard the guests speak.

"Marco!" he exclaimed, and embraced him. "Oh, Marco mio! My well-beloved cousin!"

Marco kissed him on both cheeks.

"Christopher!" he cried. "May all the gods be praised! Welcome to our household, Cousin mio! A thousand times welcome!"

CHAPTER FIFTEEN

Captured at Sea

THE Polos settled down to their old life in Venice. Again they were Noble Venetians, continuing their trade as merchants. Three more years went flying by.

Marco's life was not all given to trading. He loved his native country and wished to serve her well.

One afternoon he walked with Christopher at the Arsenal.

"They are building many galleys," Christopher observed, "but most of them are meant for war."

"War, indeed!" said Marco. "And why not? The city of Genoa threatens our trade with the East more than ever before. Do you think that we will stand by and watch her sailors plunder our ships under our very noses?"

"Hardly!" laughed Christopher.

Marco laid his hand on Christopher's arm. "Come and I will show you what else is being done to help protect Venice," he said.

He led the way across the yard to a place where another new galley was being built.

"This is larger than any of them!" Christopher said in surprise. "I wonder who is building it."

Marco smiled proudly.

"The Polos are building it, Christopher. We want it to be a part of the great Venetian fleet if war really comes. Would you like to go aboard?"

They boarded the ship and examined it from bow to stern. The vessel was built of seasoned timber. It had a hundred oars on each side. It would carry a crew of two hundred oarsmen, forty or fifty men armed with crossbows, several carpenters and caulkers, and a cook. And of course there would be a captain and his staff of officers.

Christopher stood on the half-finished deck.

"She is a most seaworthy vessel," he said. "What do you plan to name her?"

"We intend to christen her *The Valiant*," Marco replied. As they left the ship he added, "If war really begins between Venice and

Genoa, I hope she will live up to her name."

The Valiant was christened one day several weeks later. On that very afternoon the Polos learned that war between Venice and Genoa had become unavoidable.

"So *The Valiant* is to go to sea as a warship," Marco's father said sadly. "We must see that she has a brave captain and crew." He turned to Marco and laid his hand on his shoulder. "You, my son, are to be her Gentleman Commander, and I wish you Godspeed."

Marco knew that his father meant that he was to advise the captain of the boat. It was an old Venetian custom to have a Gentleman Commander on every ship in the fleet. He would be expected to be on deck, ready to be consulted by the captain when he was needed.

The day soon came for him to sail. His father and uncle and Christopher came down to the Arsenal to say good-by.

"Marco, my son," said his father, "I have bid you farewell many times in your life. It seemed a hard thing to do in Cathay, but this time it is doubly hard because I know that you will be engaged in battle."

Marco tried to comfort his old father.

"It will not be my first battle," he said, "and

fighting Italian seamen should not be as dangerous as fighting the Enchanters of the East!"

His gray-haired uncle Maffeo laughed.

"Be on your guard against them, Marco,"

he told him. "They, too, are skilled in warfare, if not in magic!"

Christopher embraced Marco, saying: "Farewell, Cousin mio! May God go with you and guard you well!"

They stood on the shore and watched *The Valiant* go sailing out to sea. It was one of sixty vessels in the proud Venetian fleet. All were under the command of an admiral and his officers. And all were made gay with colored banners flying in the wind.

There were seven thousand seamen in the Venetian fleet. On September 7th in the year 1298, they met the Genoese fleet at sea.

"Keep your banners flying!" cried the brave admiral. "But stand by to fight!"

Marco Polo stood on the deck of *The Valiant*. The fierce battle was beginning. He

[*169*]

could see the crossbows flying from ship to ship. He could hear the beating of kettle-drums and the shrill music of the fifes which were played on every ship to arouse the men to fighting pitch.

Now and then a clarion call came through from the captain of *The Valiant:* "On your guard, men! On your guard! Let your battle axes fly!"

So the heavy battle raged. On and on and on. By the middle of the day, it was easy to see that the gallant Venetians were on the losing side. Already many Venetian ships had been captured.

Marco Polo was horrified to hear that the admiral had been unable to endure the thought of defeat. Already he had killed himself by dashing his head against a ship's bench.

The Valiant was the lead ship when there came a dread command:

"STAND BY TO SURRENDER!"

Marco Polo bowed his head. He and *The Valiant* had lost the fight. So had the other men and ships in the Venetian fleet.

Soon his captors came aboard.

"Tear down the banners on this galley!" they commanded. "Let them drag in the water while you are towed backward into port!"

And so the fighting came to an end. The proud Venetian fleet was taken.

Marco Polo's moment of surrender was a bitter one. He saw the banners of his ship torn down. He saw her led backward into Genoa.

He knew that in Genoa death or a black dungeon waited to receive him.

CHAPTER SIXTEEN

The Book of Marco Polo

MARCO POLO was put in chains and led to a prison in Genoa. He thought of his father and uncle. How sad they would be when they heard what had happened to the Venetian fleet! How unhappy they would feel over the loss of *The Valiant!* And how they would worry about him when the news came that he had been cast into prison!

But they would do more than just worry, he reminded himself. They would do all they could to obtain his release.

"If I cannot find a way to escape," he said to a man beside him, "I am sure that my father and uncle will do everything possible to make the leaders of Genoa set me free."

What Marco said was true. His father and uncle tried everything in their power to bring about his release from prison. But even though they offered a princely ransom to the leaders of Genoa, those leaders refused to release Marco Polo.

Long days and weeks and months dragged on. The prison was damp and as dark as a dungeon. Because of his noble rank, however, Marco Polo was not kept in one of the murky cells reserved for common prisoners. He was permitted the freedom of the prison and the prison yard. He was also allowed to talk with his fellow prisoners. One day he met a man named Rustichello who came from the city of Pisa.

"So you are Marco Polo!" Rustichello greeted him. "I have heard that you are a man of many travels."

Marco answered him pleasantly.

"I have been to Cathay," he said. "And I have also traveled in many other countries and seen the marvels of the Eastern world."

"Tell me about your travels," said Rustichello. "I am a scribe and a scholar. Nothing could interest me more."

From that day on, it seemed to Marco Polo that the walls of the prison faded away. As he told the story of his wanderings to this man of

He imagined himself once more in golden Kanbalu

learning, he imagined himself once more in golden Kanbalu. There was nothing that he did not remember, from the Street of Singing Stars to the wine trees of Ceylon. His new friend, Rustichello, was enchanted.

"Surely," he exclaimed, "no other man from Europe has ever been where you have been!"

Marco Polo suddenly had an excellent idea. "Since you are a scribe and a scholar," he said, "I will have my father send me my copies of the records I kept for the Great Khan. From the records I will dictate the story of my travels to you and you may write it down and preserve it for all time."

Messer Rustichello was delighted.

"It will be a magnificent story!" he said. "I shall be proud to write it for you!"

And so the great work began. Instead of pitying himself because he must remain in prison, Marco Polo spent his days dictating to Rustichello the wonderful story of his adventures in the East.

Messer Rustichello began the book by saying:

"Great princes, emperors, and kings, dukes, knights, and people of all degrees who desire to get knowledge of the various races of mankind and regions of the world, take this book and cause it to be read to you.

"For ye shall find therein all kinds of wonderful things according to the description of Messer Marco Polo, a wise and noble citizen of Venice, as he saw them with his own eyes."

Day after day, the two men sat in the gray-walled prison and Rustichello wrote down the stories which Marco related to him.

Marco told him again about his long, dangerous journey across Asia to Cathay, and about the Great Khan and his palaces. He described all the countries he had visited and the routes he had used to reach them. He talked of the strange things he had seen in those far-off lands and of the people and their customs.

At last the book was finished. Soon after this a truce was signed between Venice and Genoa. Then Marco was freed and went back home to Venice.

Of course he took his book with him. Though he did not know it then, "The Book of Marco Polo" was a very important book, since it was the first one ever written which told the people of Europe about the distant countries of the East.

Many copies of the book were made and it was read by people in Venice and in other cities. It filled them with a desire to travel and to see the wonders which Marco Polo had described. But some of the people could not believe in these wonders.

"Surely!" they exclaimed, "all of these things cannot be true. Trees that give wine! Trees filled with flour from which bread can be made! An animal named a unicorn! Pure gold to be found in flowing rivers! People called cannibals who eat human flesh! These are just fairy tales."

When Marco heard men and women speak in this way, he had only one answer to make to them.

"All of this is true, my friends," he would declare solemnly. "I have not told half of what I saw."

Meanwhile Marco had married a lovely girl named Donata. They settled down in Venice and he continued his trade as a merchant. Time went on and the fame of his book spread far and wide.

At last, when Marco was an old man, he became very ill.

"Perhaps your husband will die," his friends

"I have not told half of what I saw," he declared

said to Donata. "He should admit now that the things he said in his book are untrue."

Marco turned on his couch and opened his eyes.

"I tell you once again and I swear it to be true," he said in a feeble voice, "I have not told half of what I saw. I hope that the day may come when all the world will believe my stories of the marvels of the East."

Sinking back against his pillows, he listened to the convent bells of Venice which were ringing softly. Dreamily he remembered temple bells ringing in the golden shrines of far Cathay. With a smile, Marco Polo closed his eyes.

Marco Polo's wish came true. With the passing of the years, he became respected all over the civilized world as having been a wise and honorable man. The truth of his book was proven by many travelers who followed in his footsteps. He became known as an explorer, map maker, navigator, ambassador to many lands, and the First Lord of Geography.

It took time to prove the worth of Marco Polo's adventures. He gave to the world a great new world to explore. He laid upon the hearts of men the golden spell of far-off places.

About the Author

OLIVE PRICE was born in Pittsburgh, Pennsylvania. There she went to school and college, and later took her first job—as advertising copywriter in one of Pittsburgh's largest stores. After her first trip to New York, at eighteen, she published her first book of plays. Since then, she has written over a hundred plays. In 1948, she began writing books for young people, too, and has been busy at it ever since. She likes dogs, and has a shepherd-collie for company while she is working. She also likes to poke around odd New York shops—mostly bookshops—and to explore country roads in her car.

About the Artist

FEDERICO CASTELLON was born in Alhabia, Spain. When he was seven years old, his parents left Spain and settled in Brooklyn. There he went through Erasmus Hall High School, where he took the only formal art course he has ever had. Even then, his extraordinary talent was recognized. He went abroad to study the great masterpieces of art in Spain, France, and England. Pictures were his teachers. By the time he was twenty, he was considered an accomplished master of his craft. During the war he went to China and India as a member of O.S.S. Now he is married, living in Brooklyn again, and has a young son.

About the Signature

THE PUBLISHERS have searched vainly in museums and libraries in Italy, England, and the United States for the signature of Marco Polo. It is possible that he did not know how to write, especially since he dictated "The Book of Marco Polo" to a scribe. Since no signature of his seems to be in existence, Marco Polo's name is shown in this book as it would look if written in Cantonese characters as close as possible to the Chinese of his time.

"Names That Made History"

ENID LAMONTE MEADOWCROFT, *Supervising Editor*

HANDSOME BOOKPLATES: *Send your name and address
to* SIGNATURE BOOKS, GROSSET & DUNLAP, INC., 1107 Broadway,
New York 10, N. Y., *and we will mail you, upon receipt of
ten cents to pay the cost of postage and handling, a set of
handsomely designed bookplates, each one different.*

1 Born in Venice, Italy, 1254

2 Meets his father for the fir[st] time, 1269

3 Starts the journey to the East, with father and uncle, 1271

4 Arrives at Kublai Kha[n]'s court, in Shangtu, China, 1275

10 Dies in Venice, January 9, 1324

9 Released from prison in Genoa. 1299

8 Dictates "The Book of Ma[rco] Polo" while in prison, 1[298]